INCONSPICUOUS

Walter Rothwell's Undercover
Journey During the Cold War

———————

WES CHOC

Tuscon, Arizona

Inconspicuous: Walter Rothwell's Cold War Undercover Journey

ISBN: 978-0-9964179-2-1

Book design by Bri Bruce Productions

Published by Chosen Journey Media
Tucson, AZ 85741
U.S.A.

www.weschoc.com

To Wally Rothwell himself, his late wife Thelma, his daughters Danielle and Linda, his neighbors, and to all who knew him throughout his life and times.

Who knows? Might he be that staid sphinx-type guy who made a difference—a difference that turned out to be notable of historical consequence? Or, might he have been that someone who only thrived inconspicuously in the shade and shadow of the rose?

Acknowledgements

Without the support and sacrifices of friends and family, this story would never have been told. I want to especially thank my wife, Carol, for her direct assistance in discovering various passages and paragraphs that made perfectly good sense to me, but obviously would not have made sense to nearly everyone else. These and several other red question marks throughout what I was calling the very last draft, proved essential.

Stimulating me to write this book were numerous friends many of whom read my first book *Just Dust: An Improbable Marine's Vietnam Story*. They encouraged me to keep putting words on paper whenever I would verbalize something about this interesting character, friend and neighbor named Walter Rothwell. In particular, I'd like to thank neighbors Carol Ann Rott, Bucky and Marlene Grace, Jim Tripp, and Kit and John Pierce in particular; and, Sue and Jim Opeka, Art and Janette Carr, Mary Brown, Jonathan Jackson, Mike Davis, and numerous others I've had coffee with. To these folks I extend special thanks for listening, for asking astute questions, and for inquiring about my story before I could tell them more details unprompted.

Facilitating the "how" part of publishing this book, I want to acknowledge the devotion of Tim Derrig who through personal suggestions, solid knowledge, and perpetual humor, was able to motivate me off dead center. A thank you here is insufficient recognition of this value.

Finally, I'd like to urge my children and grandchildren to read. There are so many stories to tell, and so many of these will never be written down. So, to Brian, Jared, Tyler, and to Parker, Adrienne, Keira, Camden, and Caspian, I urge you to listen, to read, to understand, to discuss, and yes, to write your own stories so others may enjoy these journeys too in times yet to come.

- Wes Choc
Tucson, Arizona
2015

Prologue

When asking Wally Rothwell about what character or image might depict his persona better than any other, I received quite a few different kinds of lengthy descriptions during our time together. Though thoughtfully considered, none of these ever clearly described the Walter Rothwell that I was listening to. There was never anything that he could easily put into a word or two. After I kept probing deeper for something more brief and tangible, he finally came up with a singular image.:

"Sphinx," he then said stoically staring at me with one of his Mona Lisa smiles. Without probing further, I looked back saying nothing except to watch him demur then explain.

The Sphinx

Steadfast, observant, staid, strong, respected were all words he modestly embraced to portray this self-image. To pry these depictions out of Wally's usual anti-self-aggrandizement attitude, was a slow, tedious conversation—successful only because I persisted.

After chiding him with a couple of James Bond type images, he would say "no, no—not like that at all. Things happened, not because I *made* them happen, rather because I knew how to *let* them happen."

This indeed was the "what" of all that was worthy to him to be sure. I felt it odd nonetheless, because while it might indeed describe him, it seemed the billboard not the character that I could actually see—that man I actually met with regularly and listened to for more than a year.

But I kept clutching a different image—an image he inferred rather than said. It seemed more a sketchy off-the-record admission from a very private person than a definition—an image of one who others simply could not easily see or appreciate …not even me for the longest time. I took notes. I connected pieces. I looked under the rug.

No, I said to myself. Though sphinx-like in some authentic ways, he is definitely not statuesque. I pondered that Egyptian metaphor and concurred there was something more mysterious about this man. But it's something less of a tangible icon to gaze upon, like a sphinx, and more like an invisible guardian—someone to appreciate rather than see.

I captured a wisp of an image early on in our conversations when he talked about the "how" of those things that were consequential to him. Sometimes it surprised even him about "how" he had to react to unpredictable events. Many of these responsive "how" behaviors were unknown or unintentionally concealed to everyone else in the world—more like inadvertent camouflage. He just blended in, faded away, casually suggesting many "who-was-that?" interludes where he was the fly whizzing around who no one noticed. For him it was like living "under the rose" or *sub rosa* …and for me, this metaphor just stuck.

The Rose[1]

First, some background.

Historically, the rose has held a deeply symbolic meaning in cultures as a symbol of creativity and power. For centuries, the literal blooming rose and its essence played repetitious roles in religious rites and ceremonies regarding things purposefully undisclosed. The rose's connotation regarding secrecy first dates back to early Greek mythology when Aphrodite gave a rose to her son Eros, the god of love. He in turn gave it to Harpocrates, the god of silence, to assure his mother's indiscretions (or those of other gods) were not inadvertently disclosed.

Later, during the Roman period of Egyptian history, the rose had become sacred to Isis perhaps in connection with the goddess Aphrodite (Venus) who used the rose in her private worship.

Still later, the Greeks and Romans both translated the Egyptian god's name Herupakhered into their own Harpocrates, regarding him by then as god of silence. The association of Harpocrates with silence and secrecy originated from this misunderstanding of Egyptian depictions of their god.

Herupakhered had been represented as a naked youth with a finger-to-mouth gesture. In Egyptian artwork this gesture imitated the hieroglyph for a child and was used to represent youth, but was misunderstood by later generations of Greeks and Romans as a gesture for silence.

Consequently, paintings and other depictions of roses on Roman banquet room ceilings were gentle warnings or at least reminders that things discussed in the room *under the rose* needed to remain *sub rosa* (i.e., not to be disclosed in any other forum). Many meetings were concluded with something akin to "this topic will remain *sub rosa*."

Colloquially, among people who understand these expressions, other similar terms came to be used within intellectual, legal, or religious venues. For example *sub vino* to alert for needed

---

[1] Much of this information was extrapolated from Wikipedia and other authoritative sources.

discretion when under the influence of wine.

Later on during the Middle Ages, a rose suspended from the ceiling inside council chambers similarly pledged those attending to secrecy.

In Christian symbolism, the phrase *sub rosa* had a special place during confessions. Pictures of roses with five petals were often carefully hand-carved into the sides or corners of confessionals, indicating conversations would remain completely confidential.

The rose is also an esoteric symbol of Rosicrucians, considered a secret brotherhood.

By the 16th century, the symbol of Henry VIII of England was the stylized Tudor rose. There was a large image of the rose covering the ceiling in private chambers where decisions of state were made in secret.

Nowadays, while the term sub rosa has weathered a history of innumerable meetings that never were recorded accurately on paper, the term is used inside the legal community and by some governments to describe off-the-record meetings. This word may be uttered, but it's seldom documented …the word itself is almost *sub rosa*.

———

There indeed may have been an imagined sphinx lurking out there—that steadfast, observant, staid, strong, respected overseer (conspicuously depicted at the end of the eastern Sahara).

Inside my own mental dialogue, I might be having this conversation. "Y'know, under there! See him? He's right there where you can't really spot him unless you know where to look."

No matter what, in my opinion, this particular sphinx inhabited a special place *subrosa* or, right there under the rose …yes,

…inconspicuously.

1

Walter Henry Rothwell Junior gasped his first breath amply blessed[1] with genetically embedded compasses that might eventually channel him ably-prepared, fine-tuned, and well-groomed in the footsteps of his theater-limelighted father and mother. That's what everybody thought anyhow. That's what the newspapers printed. That's what Walter Junior actually believed true as he grasped first-words so he could think.

Such inevitabilities could have been true ...if he had paid attention, that is.

There were distractions ...like this new little boy crossing the Atlantic.

But walking between shadows of two already so well-known could have been a steep mountain to climb anyway, especially with all that exceptional DNA so carefully emplaced. Yet these gifts never materialized how others might have foreseen.

---

[1] *Walter Henry Rothwell Jr. was born May 11, 1923, at Good Samaritan Hospital, Los Angeles, California.*

There were myriad choices …like multiple languages.

Walter Rothwell Junior, or Wally as he became known, you see, would dance upon a different stage. He would memorize different scripts.

There were erratic happenstances …like World War II.

Still, he eventually played a part—a role without auditions or memorized lines, no tickets or applause—an important role bearing different encores. Despite disconcerting discoveries along the way, he achieved more on this stage than he ever might getting his name in lights.

Though consequential, he was inconspicuous.

——————

As chance would have it, heritage was unconventional.

Among four grandparents, each spoke a foreign language (i.e., not English), traveled through multiple ports of call, crossed international borders, married, and lived where just one language, whatever it was, would never do. So, inside this familial cultural stew, it was a natural thing for his parents to inspire (permit?) environments where Wally learned there were no typical models to copy …he learned to think for himself early on.

Wally's original playbook was translated and retranslated all depending on where breakfast happened to be served that morning.

Once lingual menus were synchronized, translations and verbal nuances, manufactured slang and multilingual puns were all common dinner fare—with the main course being whatever the dialect d' jour happened to be.

Ever-changing buffets, Wally adapted to multi-scripted bills of fare.

——————

But those shadowy hiding places Wally sought as a child …those out of the way places he lived within as a youth. What about the shaded alleys he perused in the army after World War II as a young soldier ...the dimly-lit grottoes he adeptly slithered through to gain evidence or innuendo or scrap of useful hearsay? Just what were these narrow and oh-so-private paths? It didn't take long to learn camouflage or inconspicuousness—on stage or not.

It really boiled down to choices:

Thought? ...which language was best used for thinking? ... for acting? ...for laughing? ...for loving?

Secrecy? ...who was in the same room listening? ...who could be trusted?

Allegiance? ...what chevrons would emblazon his sleeves? ...which tattoos could be embedded onto his heart?

In the shadow of the rose, only one person knew for sure.

2

You see, way before Wally was even born, Walter Rothwell (Senior) was a distinguished, indeed famous man. A gifted music virtuoso, at age nine in 1880, protégé Rothwell entered the Royal Academy of Music in Vienna. Graduating with highest possible honors extraordinarily early at fifteen, he promptly became recognized by the music elite of the day.

Having personally counseled Walter in formal music education from late 1880s to early 1890s, his renowned mentor, Johannes Brahms, eventually steered young Rothwell away from being *just* a master pianist into demonstrable abilities on violin, cello, clarinet, and other instruments as well. He was a natural.

By seventeen, Walter had already ripened into a celebrated pianist throughout Germany and central Europe. Despite conspicuous appointments within the Austrian aristocracy and Royal Opera of Vienna, Brahms coaxed him to consider orchestra conducting. With Brahms' public blessing and private encouragement, Gustav Mahler, the up-and-coming conductor of the Hamburg Orchestra, accepted Rothwell as his direct understudy.

After thriving throughout these significant hurdles, Rothwell began conducting orchestra on his own throughout Europe already with indisputable advance name recognition. He drew crowds of admirers not unlike celebrities we might see in television or movies today.

By invitation, he eventually agreed to come to the U.S. in 1904, and gave 114 performances of Parsifal all around the country. Not long thereafter, on the second U.S. tour under his baton, now-famous Rothwell directed the very first American presentation of Puccini's Madame Butterfly. Garnering widespread acclaim in America, one invitation led to another and yet another ...from the biggest cities like New York, Chicago, and San Francisco to places like Cincinnati and St. Paul.

Born of Austrian and British parents, Walter Rothwell was comfortable in both English and German speaking environments—an advantage of sorts working into hierarchies of American entertainment networks. He was easily admitted into this fraternity.

While clearly admired and celebrated wherever he went, Walter Rothwell was eventually lured to accept the permanent position as the very first conductor appointed for the newly formed Los Angeles Philharmonic Orchestra in 1919 right after Sergei Rachmaninoff declined the offer. His acclaim preceded him wherever he went. By 1920, performances at Madison Square Garden regularly drew crowds of 6,000 or more per event.

———

Elizabeth Wolff had already achieved her own name recognition throughout Europe. German by birth and a dramatic soprano with a résumé preceding her, she learned Italian by singing opera. She was picked to perform the debut of Puccini's Madame Butterfly in New York in 1907. This was where diva and conductor met eye to eye on stage, hand in hand off stage, finally heart to heart one performance after another. They partied among merrymakers in music's high society. Diva Elizabeth found herself entranced by the young flamboyant California conductor.

They married in 1908 producing forage for entertainment media to scavenge upon for years.

Walter and Elizabeth became unquestionably socialites extraordinaire. But it was a complex and unpredictable lifestyle. Some days they basked in dramatic fast-paced social scenes. Other times they bathed among southern California's on-the-beach sun-set before presenting a first child, Claire, in 1918.

Once daughter Claire was followed by Walter Jr. in 1923, family life changed. Both parents' names always stayed in papers (just not at the same time), and both danced in high-end social circles (sometimes together). They were photographed with all the right people.

Conductor Rothwell and Diva Rothwell played the Hollywood Bowl to crowds sometimes numbering over 10,000

Family friends and visitors smiled when toddler Wally

restrained his lips to keep from breaking into that oft-praised grin. Though he liked grinning, the young lad really wanted to show off that dramatic white row of four front teeth with just a little, well-tuned little-boy drama, the kind he copied from mama.

First Rothwell Family Photo: California 1923, Claire, Walter Sr, Walter Jr, and Elizabeth

As Elizabeth Wolff, she had been an eminent indeed broadly famous woman inside her own world. But, as Elizabeth Rothwell, she was Walter's wife and mother of two. She was losing private center stage limelight.

Wally's at-home education was zigzagging, impacted by rival theater urgencies and well-orchestrated public admirations on one hand, and by competing family attentions and shortfalls on the other. This created contradictions amid celebrity-induced priorities—managed pandemonium.

———

Postwar times shifted outlooks too. Single sentence reminders about European reconstruction, or veteran recuperation and recovery, or Bismarck were abandoned or dismissed. Now, paragraphs were exchanged updating everyone about new speedy cars, dashing hairstyles, and faster-paced music. New books about life were being written, a new language was being spoken.

Smiles always greeted friends when *the* Rothwells showed up with a flashing 1920s era flourish. It was handled with the right glamour, at all the right places, at just the right parties. Handshakes were sought from Walter, coifs copied from Elizabeth. After all, Walter and Elizabeth were both one of *them*.

Conductor, Walter Rothwell

But each had separate journeys amid all this social traffic and family exhibition. It kept them together, yet professionally apart before and after Wally arrived on the scene. Schedules conflicted. Mother and father visited on weekdays between events—events that would take her to places far away days at a time then back again for a day or two's familial rendezvous. Fast-paced days were tightly regimented. Everything personal or private was timetabled around more public events. There were always *considerations* to respect.

By 1924-25 she was appearing on operatic stages across North America in cities like New York and Los Angeles, to small towns like Moose Jaw, Saskatchewan. A strong-willed, relentless performer, she undauntedly honored extraordinarily heavy agendas as well as more routine obligations. She had *standards* to uphold after all.

Then Elizabeth was offered a high-status engagement to perform throughout Europe. Vacillating about what such commitments would entail, she simply couldn't ignore the career implications either. Now limelighting at the top of her game, Elizabeth accepted this prestigious job but only as long as she could bring her two children with her: nine year old daughter, Claire, and four year old son, Wally. No one said no.

The role entailed unveiling of the new operatic release at the Königsberg Festival by Alban Berg, a highly anticipated and well publicized debut. However, it also meant a multi-year commitment that included intense stage exercises, extended practice sessions, including late night rehearsals and performances.

The *avant garde* Opera "Wozzeck," composed by Alban Berg was based on the three-act play by the same name by Georg Büchner. Austrian composer, Alban Berg, was arguably the most distinguished disciple of Arnold Schönberg, and became prominent during his time being part of Vienna's culturally privileged. The controversial opera Wozzeck was conceived during World War I, and had received its first stage practice performances in Berlin in 1925-26. This play was reflective of then contemporary attitudes. According to Berg: *"It deeply stirred all of Middle Europe of that period. This period was the period of Dr. Sigmund Freud, the period of Franz Kafka, the period of the rise of National Socialism. In music it was the period that saw the most violent breakdown of old ideas of melody—and, even more, of harmony. It was revolutionary, it was intellectually curious, it was unstable, and it reflected the sickness of the German soul."*

Unquestionably, Wozzeck was a landmark opera and is remembered as one of the 20th Century's most important works written by one of the most worthy composers for these times. History has validated Berg as the most widely performed opera composer among Viennese musicians. This was indeed a big debut and a big deal.

So, to be offered the lead soprano role of Marie was a profound professional opportunity for already-acclaimed Elizabeth Rothwell. After accepting this quite demanding offer, the three of them crossed the Atlantic and relocated to the German (then East Prussian) city of Königsberg (today, this city is called Kaliningrad and is part of Russia).

———

Rehearsals began promptly for performers on stage as well as the orchestra. Inevitable backroom dramas, offstage rumors, and human collisions commenced. These too were part of the game. As the theater company congealed into friendships ...as musicians and performers solidified into their roles ...as endless practices commenced, the troupe predictably encountered predictable setbacks of skill and talent as well.

One of these was how to fill the role of lead performer Marie's young son. None of the children auditioning had either the stage presence or the voice range needed for the part. Typically, boys old enough to perform well onstage faced deepening voices or awkward tenor tones; younger boys were often not disciplined enough or lacked talent. The part for this Wozzeck play required not only a very young youth with a controlled onstage attitude, but a boy who understood both melody and dissonance. It wasn't about merely singing in tune with others like every other boy who tried out for the role tried to do. Most seemed unable to grasp this nuance.

At this point several character alterations were being considered to overcome this obstacle until someone suggested casting Wally.

Over Elizabeth's initial rejection of the idea, she finally acquiesced for young Walter Rothwell to be auditioned for the part. Wally exceeded expectations with nonchalance onstage coupled with an obviously inherited range of boy-soprano tones.

Wally was a natural—even dissonance was not a challenge. He got the job! This might have been the most conspicuous role he would ever play. Now-proud mother Elizabeth didn't have to make everyone aware of her son's presence. He had a good time garnering attentions of others, not to mention staying up late and appreciating applauses with spontaneous grins.

At highly anticipated Königsberg Festival, Wozzeck was performed two times to receptive audiences and subsequent wide acclaim.

In a special presentation, Wally was singled out for his unique contributions on stage and awarded a wreath with emblazoned banners declaring "to the young and talented artist, Walter Rothwell". These ribbons are framed and hang in his home to this day.

Meanwhile in the U.S. the atmosphere during the 1920s was progressing further into now on-edge ambiances not seen before. Those with wealth learned to spend their earnings for new inventions. Those with stealth learned to manage their skills into jobs never seen before. Those with health learned once again how to clutch "good times" from those war-ravaged headlines of that World War now past.

Everyone was thriving. Everyone seemed happier with faster automobiles, taller buildings, more radio news and entertainment, fresher music, abundant named personalities. There was so much more news to consume, ideas to consider.

But Father died—passing away before Wally could remember his dad's image, abandoning too soon early memories that might have been. In his 50s, Walter Senior had been seized by a heart attack while driving his

Elizabeth (as Marie) with Wally onstage

car on the highway to Santa Monica where he liked to go to study music scores. For those on the American West Coast, it was a headline event.

It was of course an unexpected development for loyal fans and friends living in Los Angeles who knew the Rothwells so well, as well as for his family now in Königsberg. After all, it was quite a newsworthy event. But because of daily stage commitments and extraordinary challenges with trans-Atlantic traveling by ship during the 1920s, Elizabeth had to decide, and agreed not to return to the U.S. for this 1927 event.

Where there were once rows of standing ovations and endless roars of "bravo!" in California, there were now closed eyes and mourning among those who once cheered and cherished Walter's work. They felt the void of his departure immediately.

———

Meanwhile, much political uneasiness and nationalistic party grumblings were going on in Germany by the mid-1920s as well. Community behaviors were changing in Europe, individuals' activities were more scrutinized by others; heritages were questioned. Though folks recognized these undercurrents, most didn't know how to alter their usual conduct—or even what it all really meant.

Though born in California, Wally developed his primary thinking vocabulary in German even before he started school. Progressing through grade school, he adapted as any other boy might do, into this odd world he was now living in. Luckily, young Walter Rothwell was intelligent, quickly grasping subtleties and nuances from histories he studied. This was especially useful since he learned how to do two things at once—like listening to Verdi while reading about the Thirty Years War in Europe (had he lived in California, he probably would have been studying the American Civil War).

And too, he was good at recognizing (and using) all those vivid Italian words and phrases his mother verbally manipulated before, during, and after her onstage emotional arias. Of course she would pridefully translate these for Wally as he was mastering both German grammar and literature. So he learned more than a little Italian on the side as well. By now there were three distinctive words for every noun, verb, and adjective in their household all depending on the mood of the moment. German was first and academic, Italian was often used at dinner or for more demonstrative discussions, and English was fallback for more private exchanges. And, there was never just one thing to do at a time …ever! Juggling priorities was part of the norm just as juggling language had become.

———

Times were tough. American prosperity disintegrated into dust bowls in the Plains and bread lines in the cities, Wally saw swastikas on flagpoles and endless rows of uniformed troops. His education outside the classroom was important of course; there were so many unanswered questions. Even Wozzeck had been publicly condemned by the new socialists.

In 1930 his mother had fallen in love with the Swiss composer and poet, Robert Bosshart. But with all the political festering going on around them, Elizabeth and Robert decided to move from Königsberg to Switzerland after they married in 1932. This neutral country was a natural choice and a place perceived to be a safer haven for many Europeans, and especially for those in art and music. The Bossharts picked a small city beautifully set in the Italian Swiss Alps called Lugano, the perfect place for Robert and Elizabeth considering all the commotion and clatter of European adjustments to hard-to-understand politics and human reactions.

Robert was a private man devoted to his music and poetry, and Lugano was an extremely quiet, ideal rural town in southeastern Switzerland very near the Italian border. Being a man insistent on his solitude and tranquility without any distractions, it was determined it would be better that both children attend public schools elsewhere: Claire in Zurich and Walter in the village of Trogen (northeastern Switzerland near Lake Constance).

Large numbers of dependents attended these schools because mounting tensions in Germany had disrupted so many households. Wally lived with three other boys at the instructor's *pension* or residence. Arrangements as these were mutually beneficial since teachers earned extra money doing this. It was a safe alternative to Germany and a practical alternative for the Bossharts.

By now, Elizabeth and Robert were living modestly in Lugano with few assets or opportunities. Elizabeth had ended her singing career and spent most of her time writing down Robert's music for him by hand. Many were piano versions of his operas, or other synopses for piano that needed recording onto paper.

German Poet and Composer, Robert Bosshart

14

Set in the shadows of more rounded Italian Alpine terrain and wide extended valley vistas, they called the little house overlooking Lake Lugano in the distance, *Villa Merlin*, referring back to memories of storybooks and the most supreme sorcerer of all—a fantasy Robert invited the family to share. As the 1930s inched by, the imagination so produced helped the isolation from all else that seemed fictional or invented going on far to the north.

When Wally and Claire returned for holidays, it may have been special, but it was also a subdued occasion for them. Both children were embracing adulthood with their own opinions about art, family, and politics. Yet stepfather Bosshart produced neither the welcome nor personal warmth that a home visit might expect. Beyond Robert's chosen isolation, it may have also been that father number two could never take the place of father number one in both child's eyes.

———

Not being completely comfortable at home led to another new adventure for Wally. The Swiss had been recruiting youth to work on farms. This was useful because so many young men who lived in the country had been drafted into the Swiss army. It was also useful since there was so much work to be done that farmers could not do it all by themselves. In particular, twelve to fifteen year old boys were encouraged to spend their summers on farms; and, he did just that through his early teenage years.

For Wally it meant living and working on a dairy farm in nearby mountains. Most days were spent tending cowsheds, milking cows, and cleaning out animal debris. He also spent part of his day mowing grass and grains to store in the farmer's barns for winter use, and baling hay. While there were few other teenagers his age working on this particular farm, he was reminded how important volunteering in this way was for Switzerland. He earned respect for his labor from both the farmer and his wife as well as from his own mother and step-father.

As a byproduct of this labor, Wally became physically strong and able. During these formative years, he also transferred

Wally (center) and friend on the farm

his summer prowess into school-year athletics. At Trogen High School, he was a team member for most track and field events; but his first choice was the Decathlon. In one event, his team had to run three tracks (100 meter, 200 meter, 400 meter runs), plus discus, javelin, broad jump, and high jump.

However, his number one favorite sport was skiing. There was nothing that could take the place of slashing those downhill snow-laden banks of challenge at speeds that froze his grinning face and cooled his inflating lungs with high altitude Swiss air. He became an excellent skier, and performed well on his high school ski team.

———

Unexpectedly, in 1937 in his late 30s, Robert Bosshart died in ill health. Everything changed once again, and Elizabeth seriously thought about what she would now do for a living and about how she could continue residing in the beloved little fairy tale home in Lugano, *Villa Merlin*.

So it was during this time, she applied for various positions in the music field. But she really aspired to become a voice instructor, and so applied to the Lucerne Academy of Music. After due deliberation near the end of 1937, the Academy made her a very attractive offer, the kind she wanted to receive. She willingly accepted. Elizabeth now became more aggressive trying to sell their Lugano home, and finally relocated to Zurich by early 1938 where this musically gifted lady lived and worked until she retired in the 1950s. She passed away in 1970.

Elizabeth Bosshart had been successful. She was regularly sought as the instructor extraordinaire at the prestigious Lucerne Academy. Among several protégés, her star pupil was Edith Mathis who became a specialist in Mozart opera, and eventually a celebrity in her own right. Edith debuted performing The Magic Flute in 1956 after perfecting her craft under Elizabeth. Edith progressed into an expansive and famous career throughout Europe for many years.

Meanwhile in 1938, Swiss-neutral Lucerne was about the most practical place to be as European political threats were triggering other countries to take sides against each other.

———

Wally's sister Claire stayed on living in Zurich after she graduated from high school in 1937 for only a short while. She decided to move to the Sorbonne in France near Paris. But after two years, perhaps due in part to the obvious unpredictability of political tensions, she chose to relocate back to Los Angeles where she eventually married and went on to have two children.

———

By now Trogen was Wally's home. He was isolated, in high school, and wasn't sure exactly where his education might lure him. Between 1938 and 1942, he had become independent in spirit and authentically Swiss-oriented. But of late he was becoming more contemplative about what prospects the world might present him.

Living at the edge of this tiny Swiss island, an ocean of tit-for-tat European devastation was encircling him. It was depressing, but yet safe despite a rising tide of triumphs to the north. Amid ravaging bombs, troop movements, and disheartening headlines, there was simply no place else for him to consider going.

3

As late 1930s evolved into early 1940s, now an older teenager, Wally became even more autonomous in spirit. He progressed through each grade doing quite well academically. Studying inside a structured Swiss culture meant acquiring proficiency in both French and German side by side. But an internal side-effect was afflicting his identity. Was he Swiss? Was he German? Was he American? Most often it depended upon to whom he was speaking, or what the news headline d' jour happened to be.

By now a second world war had infected and overwhelmed Europe and East Asia.

He received a Swiss Army draft notice twice while in high school because they thought he surely must be Swiss. Both times, his passport proved vital for avoiding the draft.

———

Outside classrooms, he tried weaving his interests in music and theater developed over the years into other contemporary aspects of life. There were so many reasons and indeed underlying talent to suggest there might be some future on stage. From many inside as well as outside the family, there were also expressed expectations that he likely would embrace something maybe even musically classical.

Wally Rotwell's First Passport Photo

But his hands were too small to play concerto. So when he did play keyboards, he monopolized all the black keys on the piano. It was easier to feel those black keys—besides, he was stirred by, even attracted to sounds of sharps and flats—sounds his mom said were "beneath her" and sounded like "junk." It was dissonance plus rhythm! It was contemporary!

No matter, he was always in a hurry, so much so that he just couldn't survive piano lessons. He abandoned formal instruction altogether. Despite symphonic genes, a concert pianist he was not; a little boogie-woogie protégé on the black keys? Maybe.

It was during these early war years, he began listening to contemporary jazz—a lot! He took what raw skill he retained from keyboards and manipulated those black key boogie-woogie tunes and honkytonk styles. He particularly liked the music of Oscar Peterson and Meade Lux Lewis. His eyes caught fire when fingers ignited those sharps and flats.

Eyelids closing, cooling just for a moment, Wally to this day muses how Lewis' "Honky-tonk Train Blues" is the one 1920s' tune he still remembers with most heartfelt fondness.

Anyone who knew Wally knew jazz was tattooed on his soul. One time much later on in 1952 while tinkering on the piano in both New Orleans and Chicago jazz styles over years past led to an odd gauntlet thrown down by long-time high school classmate, Walter Leumann. Wally was visiting his mother in Zurich and had looked up his old buddy.

Reminiscing old music events and shared memories with him, Wally was egged on to make a record. For a couple francs per hour, recording studio time could be rented not far from where they were having coffee. Though self-conscious and nervous, he agreed and ended up producing a single unrehearsed record demonstrating about fifteen minutes worth of artistically improvised jazz tunes and phrases on the piano. Wally, to this day, still has this 78 record to play for anyone who has a phonograph.

———

But early 1940s were taxing times in Europe. Trying hard to grasp rationales and subtleties of international affairs, he tried to figure out what was going on all around Switzerland. Media proclamations about the mortalities and moralities of war were perplexing. Particularly, being American, the complicatedness of events became overwhelming. His peers in school would dutifully take their oaths—some joining up before they graduated.

Without direct parental upbringing during these formative years, he discovered his own brand of resourcefulness using academic role models, friends, and books. He gained an independent spirit on his own scrutinizing positions, propaganda, and politics. The "what" and "where" of events were evident, the "why" was not. Although he could read both French and German newspapers, no one could explain his hard questions using either language.

Switzerland remained an island umbrella-ed from devastating poisonous rains flooding the rest of Europe. Wally kept eyes and ears open—eyes trying to focus on words as he turned the pages in his books—and ears listening to dissonances of a jazzed up world—as deluging events outside a protected Swiss window fogged up both sight and sound.

No amount of professors' instructional rhythms could make harmony from these illogical sounds all around him. But education continued as scheduled nonetheless amid discords of war.

Walter Rothwell Jr. graduated on time from Trogen high school in 1942 now ready to take on the world—at least he thought he was ready. One thing about being ready, if you don't know exactly what you're ready for, it's easy to stand tall and lift your chin as if you did.

Though he recognized eventually he might likely have to serve a military role, he chose to enter law school. A provisional draft deferment accompanied the decision—and a choice that seemed valid at that moment. Since international affairs and competing legal systems among European players intrigued him, he reasoned his own value might be augmented if he had some credentials to put on the table—no matter what occupation enticed him later. At 19, there are so many forks in the road.

Being athletic, he also rationalized he might have a more physical role to play among military options somewhere inside these ongoing political quagmires …yet unsure what they might be. Besides, before he could plan out any realistic life mission, he had to determine how he fit into what was happening around him in the first place. So, he chose to keep in shape.

In winter he skied, in summer he bicycled, in between he ran or climbed or competed in track and field events at school. Before his mother moved to Zurich, he would bicycle from Trogen to Lugano, over a hundred miles on curvy roads through rugged country. Sometimes he'd even hang on to the back bumper of trucks to gain efficient distance and save muscle. He wasn't a rebel, he was an explorer!

But the war! So many questions left unanswered. For example, why didn't negotiation work? Why couldn't heads of state talk to each other? But war simply went on and on without any end in sight. Canadian author, Margaret Atwood, who's written many books using historical backdrops, once said, "War is what happens when language fails." Wally contemplated the complicatedness of it all in four different languages, but still couldn't translate any of the reasons why.

Surely there was a worthy role for him to play. Thinking in four languages didn't help; surely he had other abilities to offer. It was like no one could see him.

4

The world was changing like it never had before. European landscapes were obliterated, borders redrawn, alliances reformed. Just who and why was this aggressive Hitler tyrant amassing troops and power? What had he hoped to achieve, and at what cost? What did Swiss neutrality mean in Europe; why was it honored at all? Why had the Sudetenland been so important? What was the U.S.'s role supposed to be in all this?

Wally gained only a half-answer to every single question but these were swapped for two new questions every day—dizzying struggles for this analytical mind to muse.

As Prague, Poland, and Pearl Harbor became repetitious at-meal news topics, teenage indecision was replaced by volunteerism or by the draft for able-bodied youth in the U.S.—with parents smothering themselves with what-if questions at home hiding despondency for their children's future. For Wally, adulthood coincided head-on with these recent political confrontations that had turned bloody just a few miles away.

In the early 1940s, in Trogen he found himself

geographically surrounded by now-famous names of people and places of significance. Repeatedly, he reevaluated the then-evolving consequences being reiterated in classrooms, echoed in newspapers. High school distractions about these incomprehensible events turned into college confrontations and debates about principles, about ethics, about conscience.

Young American men living in Europe were by U.S. law subject to conscription and were indeed drafted. But Wally remained draft-deferred once he entered law school in 1942.

Previous devotions to "international affairs" adapted into "international law" as he progressed through college coursework and deepened his pervading gut appreciation for strife and resolution on a larger canvas.

English radio updates named Belgian or Danish towns most folks couldn't recognize let alone pronounce. German gains in Czech countryside were headlines one day, French retreats the next footnoted by those mysterious North African sojourns. Commentators made sidebar comments here and there about ships sinking in the North Sea.

Maps were everywhere. So many geography lessons were conducted so often that yesterday's bizarre-sounding now-outdated placenames on the radio were replaced by distinct even more exotic-sounding ones this morning.

Depending upon the news source or the country of news origin, the "take" on what was going on appeared to be a competition between self-righteousness or ultimate blame—not necessarily for understanding.

Trying to read between the lines of weekly magazine editorials was made even more challenging by Italian innuendo or American intention or Soviet Russian caveat or English cheekiness so much that most Europeans couldn't follow them logically. Wally explored the nuances.

Bars and cemeteries were busy backdrops for reunions … and speculations …and heated altercations.

Emotions ran deep.

Information mishmash churned daily.

Wally thrived within this bi-cultural Swiss environment attending Zurich classes using German, and in Geneva using French. He had just finished the third year of law school in 1945 when he faced this pervasively bleak world—a world pockmarked, blood-stained, and culturally in stews of sour turmoil.

With two semesters of school to go, it all changed for him as he contemplated what it might mean wading into that stew himself.

Wally, the Skier

Everything seemed so empty. Was it that he could not see others? Or, that they could not see him?

Standing tall, he looked around contemplating, reasoning, looking for melodies where there was only silence. Real solace came on the slopes. He had joined the ski team, and this effort gave him personal reprieve—comfort inside his own private world, sluicing downhill on these beautiful white mountain slopes— rugged barriers that wrapped this island of isolated Swiss security. Except for cross-border immigrants who brought their stories with them, Switzerland had been shielded from the contagions of war.

Among the British, German and French, things were more discouraging particularly among older folk. Repetitive reminiscing of all those 1920s and 1930s now-remembered basics were retranslated over breakfasts or beers, over border barricades or balcony banisters into new connotations. "Things will just never be the same again."

Raised shoulders, pinched lips, and slowly closing eyelids ended most casual conversation.

No one could redefine let alone rewrite such brutal histories just witnessed. Europe had now transformed irreparably into something less recognizable. In most conversations folks had, there were lots of "we shoulda's" and "they oughta's" and "if I were you, I woulda's..." in every other sentence. From the elderly, it sounded like advice; from youth it may have been sour laments. But despite how such words were clothed, these verbal images were more likely worn with no other rationale than to give mutual assurance to the other that each was still alive ...and standing up ...attired. Nakedness and death had become friends.

There was a new European map. There were Communists. Atomic bombs. Stockpiles of unused weapons, tanks, and jeeps. American soldiers occupied street corners everywhere. There were missing people, mass graves. Bridges and buildings seemed to teeter. Roads needed replacing.

President Roosevelt had just died.

Wasn't the war over? Or, was it just a new chapter?

In spring 1945, through Wally's scrutinizing eyes, new choices were emerging.

Being left behind was his youth and naïveté, the comfort of family and school, the protection of Switzerland.

It was not just a new fork in the road, he knew choices were consequential as never before.

5

By May war in Europe ended. Even though not surrounded by many Americans, he stored things American in his heart including the English language and dinnertime family stories—layered with things German and Italian. Though "President Truman" had by now entered everyone's vocabularies, Wally sustained Swiss tattoos on his soul as well including the German language.

Indistinguishable from either country's native speakers, he was probably German to anyone at markets or on the bus. He probably could even sip coffee in one of those ubiquitous French cafés camouflaged by any specific cultural identity to anywhere else. He just blended in with whatever crowd he was in.

After his draft deferment was cancelled, he was drafted by June. Though living in Switzerland with German clearly his first-use language, he was still a U.S. citizen and very much now needed in East Asia.

———

Because the U.S. Consulate General in Switzerland kept track of U.S. citizens living in-country, Wally had been identified on their list of eligible draftees. It was during this time, the call-up for more troops was delivered to the Consulate principally due to activities going on in the Far East.

The 22-year-old was given thirty days' notice to report for duty.

Though the war had technically ended, outright jubilation was quelled by monumental tasks for re-acclimating, rebuilding, and re-establishing family ties throughout Europe. On the other hand, Japan took over headlines; so for American young men Wally's age, it meant more unknowns to contemplate while witnessing how long festering wounds might take to heal right in his own backyard. These became tasks of acquiescence and adaptation.

———

Back when travel was restricted for Americans during the war, getting out of Switzerland used to be daunting. But now in a matter of weeks, he reported in at U.S. Army, European Operations headquarters personal office in Paris an hour early.

Although there were not a large number of young men reporting in, there were a handful of other "American-borns" hanging out and waiting with the identical purpose as he that day.

Waiting for doors to open, he stood around and made conversation with another waiting draftee of Norwegian descent, named Boe. Though officially just as American as Wally, Boe's English was mediocre, certainly less than average, so they conversed back and forth in German and French as best they could since English didn't work. Because Norwegian was a Germanic language, German ended up being more comfortable for both of them. They wondered exactly when the doors would open.

Although they were intending to report in at the U.S. Army's Personnel Office on the correct day, it turned out to be a French national holiday, Bastille Day; and, virtually everything was closed including the Personnel Office.

Everything being shut down for the day was a surprise since the holiday had not been observed during wartime. So, this year, 1945, it was an especially notable holiday for everyone French, and everyone French was indeed ready to celebrate. Evidently, the personnel office got word too late to let this crop of draftees know.

"We'll need to come back tomorrow," Boe lamented.

"Let's go get something to eat, maybe a drink," Wally urged.

"Well, at least a beer. I'm really thirsty. You like pretzels?"

So he and Boe decided to celebrate with all others on the street, French or not, who were partying during these annual festivities. Perhaps reporting in on the 15th would do instead, but that was a Sunday, so maybe Monday should work.

Their conversations just expanded from there. They had a few more things to commiserate about as they angled their way into a standup-only crowded bar. They dodged well-wishers spilling their beers as barmaids lugged around trays of frothing mugs above their shoulders.

Bastille Day drew crowds to virtually every such gathering place in the country over this special midsummer weekend. With repetitious backslapping, loud-mouthing, smoke-wafting, girl hugging, glass lifting engagements dancing all around, he and Boe became privately entangled in more pleasant, old-friend-story type conversations once they decided to postpone resolving exactly which day they would report in.

Meanwhile, clinking glasses, laughing, and moving chairs harmonized with raucous undulating layers of voices and smoke.

While progressing into beer number two, their self-styled serious v. snickering animated stories caught a few eyes elsewhere in the bar neither of them noticed. The barmaid must have mistook he and Boe for being some German Gestapo stay-behind agents or something as they were both north European in appearance with opaque non-French accents. Besides they weren't really celebrating like everyone else seemed to be.

Wally and Boe had no idea what was going on when three serious-faced men labored through the crowds into this bar packed three to one for every stool. Eventually these uniformed men made contact with the busy barmaid who casually waved her hands toward the corner where Wally was downing beer number three. Six sober eyes pointedly elbowed their way toward the corner never taking hungry eyes from their prey.

"What is your name, and what are you doing here?" the tall in-charge military police officer asked Boe in French. Frightened, Boe looked at his new friend for translation as Wally was wiping his frothy lips from the last of that third glass. Wally decorated his face with a polite smile to avoid unnecessary confrontation. Boe retained his just-found round-eyed intensity with an edge of panic evidenced by furrowed brows and raised eyelids.

Wally then chimed in using well-groomed French, "it's all right, we're just having a good time, sir" and went on to disclose their names, where they had been the day before, and the fact that they were both American. But the in-charge MP cut him off. The other two MPs closed in, lips pinched, eyes frowning.

In French, the officer stared at them with one raised eyebrow catching Wally midsentence. "Your French is too good, you are not American and neither of you are French; that's for sure. Please stand up. Now!" His voice was calm and low, just loud enough to be heard. His hands braced his waist on both sides to establish the correct pose to assure control and compliance.

The second MP grabbed Boe's arm tugging on him to comply. "But sir…" Boe grimaced in German, as he conceded "…we're just having a beer." Boe's suddenly serious German-ness was misunderstood. Tugs turned into yanks as the third MP grabbed Wally's arm. "What are you doing to us…" but Boe's trailing words were overlapped by the in-charge French MP's shriller and now-heated voice.

"No. Come with us! We'll see about this at the stationhouse. Now!"

The three military police proceeded to arrest Wally and Boe. Others nearby momentarily turned their heads toward them, gave way, but said not a word; such arrests were, after all, not that uncommon. Their arms were held tightly as they were then ushered out of the bar pushing other merrymakers momentarily aside and eventually escorting them to the police-wagon that took them to MP headquarters.

Both of them were thoroughly interrogated, entirely in French.

Wally explained several times about how they were both American draftees along with their mutual impending orders to report on the 14th. They both produced identification papers and passports. After some discussion about this year's Bastille Day festivities and office closures, ultimately the grimacing in-charge MP admitted the error and released them very late that night, too late for beer number four.

After returning to the transient barracks, they mingled with several others who were in the same waiting predicament. An in-charge army sergeant said Tuesday would now be a better check-in date for everyone, and explained where various report-to offices were located.

Tuesday morning's small crowd of Americans got up, shaved and showered, and finally checked in to their respective duty offices on the 17th. He never saw Boe again.

After Wally took his oath, completed paperwork, and received orientation about what was going to happen next, he and a couple others were transported to the training grounds about two hours away. Upon arrival he joined a group of a dozen other draftees already there. They mingled exchanging stories about where they were from and their journeys getting there.

All members of the boot camp platoon were given army-style buzz-cut haircuts then ushered in typical new rookie soldier formations to receive uniforms, underclothing, sleeping gear, tooth brushes, and finally assigned places to sleep.

Real training would begin the next day. Everyone would be ready!

———

For the U.S., actual army training in Europe was set up in central France at a place called Fontainebleau. Located on graciously beautiful grounds about thirty-five miles southeast of central Paris, the setting overflows with evocative stories of historical importance—stories that go back centuries.

Starting around the 12th Century, French kings used the picturesque countryside as a getaway haven from Paris. A formidable castle at Fontainebleau itself was built early in the 16th Century, with renovations and embellishments generously added by subsequent monarchies. Napoleon and subsequent French heads of state appreciated the magnificence of these huge grounds (larger in square miles than Paris itself) so much it became the appropriate locale for generals and prime ministers to meet whether for secret agreements, treaties, or mere private rendezvous.

After World War II ended, Fontainebleau became center for postwar allied military purposes including several NATO operations. It would go on to become the go-to meeting place for many yet-to-occur high level political conferences over the next decade.

Very athletic, Wally thrived through the various tangibly demanding drill exercises and weapons instruction. Eventually physical drills were replaced by more specific Army-type training and tactics as well as a great deal of marching around in cadence. Basic training was completed in eight weeks, and by late summer it was time for specialty instruction.

Among these new soldiers, especially those without specialties that could shelter them from immediate assignments to the Far East, a great deal of speculation centered on when and how they would be heading east.

The war in Europe was of course over, and military consciousness became immediately oriented toward Japanese warfare tactics. The Pacific theater abruptly replaced Germany in significance in newspapers and magazines. In fact, Wally himself was fully expecting an assignment to eastern Asia to occur promptly. Donning his army uniform, he stood tall acquiescing to changing circumstances with all the others. He wondered if he would study any of the tonal languages in that part of the world.

Although things Japanese captured headlines prominently one particular morning, at the last minute the operations sergeant administering assignments assessed what value Wally's linguistic skills might have in postwar Europe. Inside a last-minute deliberation process, the sergeant decided to cancel the transfer. Wally was left in limbo for hours not knowing why, as all the others packed their bags.

Considering substantial war cleanup and complicated political aftermaths throughout Europe, there was also an underappreciated requirement surfacing inside the army hierarchy—something the operations sergeant had just learned about. At a meeting earlier that morning, it was disclosed that there were too few soldiers with any kind of in-depth linguistic abilities.

Wally was now tagged.

In retrospect it just made sense, but nobody could've predicted that fork in the road.

Over the next few days in mid-September, Wally was approached about these new European themes and roles he might play in rather vague terms. Even though he wondered about what these imprecise assignments yet to come might mean, the possibilities intrigued him. His being singled out suggested something so …private …secret.

While he had a pretty good grasp of international law and only limited actual war knowledge, he was particularly naïve about the idiosyncrasies of army intelligence, fact-gathering, and all those high-level international political promises he was reading about—not to mention undisclosed postwar responsibilities agreed upon by the United States with West European allies.

He was getting a taste of who-can-you-trust?-type mentalities exhibited by enlisted and officers alike. He detected shadowy activities going on—a mysteriousness no one talked about.

This is where the ingredients of Wally's linguistic fare captured the appetite of this specialized group of postwar professionals. The kitchen had been heating up with postwar cleanups and crackdowns. The war may have been officially over, but sorting out residual activities left behind in this part of the world was complicated, messy, unpredictable.

More specifically, because of language fluencies (English, German, French, and Italian), plus three years in international law at universities in Geneva and Zurich coupled with his doing well in basic training, his assignment to the elite CIC (Counter Intelligence Corps) was eventually revealed.

At first, Wally didn't fully grasp just what this group did.

Looming war threats in the 1930s brought expansion of the Corps of Intelligence Police (CIP) back to active World War I levels. The entry of the U.S. into World War II in 1941 brought further expansion and a new name, the CIC, effective January 1942. More than 500 officers and 4,400 non-commissioned agents were authorized. The CIC recruited those with legal, police or other investigative backgrounds, particularly looking for foreign language skills. Special CIC teams had been created during WWII in Europe, in large part from Military Intelligence Service personnel. However, since there was never enough multi-lingual staff, local interpreters were often recruited to fill voids.

As Wally was completing his interim army-oriented training, he asked questions about what the duties of the CIC were.

The CIC's mission during the war focused on top secret, critically important issues dealing with intelligence as well as efforts to understand enemy intentions. Once the war was over, the mission shifted to parallel issues fixated toward lingering postwar Nazi activities on one hand, and newly developing issues with the Soviet Union (or USSR, now known as Russia), on the other.

He grasped the "words" of the mission, more or less, but still didn't really know what he was going to be doing. Not many other soldiers, civilians or local citizens knew exactly what the CIC actually *did* either.

With virtually no preparation or training whatsoever, Wally's résumé evidently preempted any more tailored instruction that might need to receive—instruction on surveillance, interrogation, or other observational techniques—all because of this conspicuous vacuum of inherent language skills among U.S. army personnel.

It was now *his* time to pack up—right person, right place. One of a kind, he was needed in Germany; he was needed now!

6

Basic training was done. Vague previews of where he was going next had followed. The in-charge officer finally explained that Private Rothwell was assigned to a base near Frankfurt, Germany. He'd joing a small army staff who worked on intelligence issues, things like surveillance and searching for former Nazis.

As descriptions crystalized, it seemed a lot of paper shuffling at first, only interesting perhaps because so much was top-secret. Still, now the war was over, it seemed anti-climactic, less consequential.

Learning Nazis needed to be filtered out of German society was a fairly easy concept to get; but, grasping the "how" part wasn't so clear.

———

As instructed, he packed his duffel to leave first thing the next morning on already-arranged transportation. After a stack of pancakes and five strips of bacon, official orders were issued. Within minutes he was a passenger in the jeep anticipating this 300 mile eastbound road trip.

His mind whizzed through what-if questions faster than the jeep could carry them on narrow roads—roads pockmarked with mortar holes and general neglect. After passing through the border checkpoint into Germany with no delay, the jeep crossed the Rhine stopping in Frankfurt only for gas and lunch. The driver knew the roads to take. There was only prophylactic silence inside engine noise and shifting gears. Rubble and pushed-aside debris were often prevalent in towns—undamaged little houses and stores caught one's eyes as exceptions. People were roaming around, it seemed without purpose. The driver engaged in no conversations; Wally figured his what-if questions would be answered in due time.

He was being relocated to a small and discreet military base called the 970th CIC Group tucked away in a rural valley near Frankfurt. Still an army private naïve to implications of these new assignments but psychologically determined to make some sort of difference, he reported for duty standing snappy tall.

Upon arrival few people spoke. After billeting was assigned to live in, he was ordered to report in to the colonel next morning. While eating dinner alone in the mess hall, he found himself eyeing others, wondering what exactly their jobs might be. Spies?

But things were different; it didn't correspond with any typical army-image either.

Not particularly familiar with the acronym "CIC" until the initials were decoded for him, he acknowledged confidentiality and military use of the word, intelligence. Yet, he remained unsure what his own role might be. On one hand, a sense of the unknown was tempting his what-if feelings while a sense of purpose was germinating inside his gut as well. It wasn't like he was hungry for action, or starving for recognition. It was just about this road less traveled. It was the intrigue.

On edge, he didn't sleep well that first night contemplating what unanticipated risks might turn out to be.

———

That first morning he restrained nervousness going to the mess hall. Immediately after scrambled eggs and bacon, he exited the cafeteria doors donning his army cap, squinting into the morning sun. Though this mystique was alluring, his stomach re-scrambled the eggs. Yet, his inner spirit surged with a sense of stealth.

Despite these apprehensions and zigzagging among unremarkable look-alike buildings, he made his way to the colonel's office without speaking to anyone.

Inside the double-door, there were a half dozen hand-shaking greetings in a group mixed with what must have been both enlisted and officers. Not that rank was totally ignored; it just seemed to matter less. In the army, soldiers became ultra-sensitive to bars and stripes very quickly upon induction. The absence of rank insignia was disconcerting—after all, how does one determine important issues at hand if you don't know the rank for the source of information? He was seated and told to wait.

Wally observed who listened to whom, and began thinking to himself. Wearing olive green tops and pink trousers, not only did they look alike, they looked more formal. He knew not everyone could be an officer, but they looked like it. They wore metallic U.S. insignias on their collars, but no bars or birds or stars. Age was the best defining characteristic to suggest rank.

He learned later when dealing with intelligence matters, it was better to look like an officer whether one or not. It gave stature and reinforced general secrecy. Besides, for some matters, it was better not perceived as "grungy enlisted."

Eventually he met the man in charge. Oldest in the room, the colonel did the most talking and the least listening. It seemed more like a business team than military infrastructure. Even language was less rigid, more spontaneous. No one barked commands—only the word "sir" was mixed with otherwise casual conversation. Over time, actual rank became clear by word choices and responses used; otherwise it appeared immaterial even though of course it was not.

The day proceeded at a preset fixed pace of introductions, private chats, and meetings, one after the other. Orientation underway, he learned he was assigned as an investigating field agent in a rather insignificant county in southwestern Germany, living in some little village.

But he still had no idea exactly what all this meant.

The second morning was more rigidly-paced once breakfast plates were bussed.

At 9:30 he was issued CIC credentials. There was paperwork. There were admonitions about secrecy and diplomacy. There were human sensitivities. Even though most conversations were impromptu and spontaneous in appearance, rationales for certain missions became more acute, more logical—certain salient points were repeated perhaps just for impact value for those new like Wally. Stories were told to illustrate what-if scenarios.

Before lunch, detailed narratives describing personality types who might pose threats to the West on one hand (like Nazis, gestapo, or their sympathizers) and explanations about those who were responsibly reconstructing postwar Germany on the other (i.e., activities supported by Western governments) were repetitiously pounded into the sessions. This took more than an hour and was intense. "You have to pick these guys out walking down the street. No one will be there helping you to do this." After thick soup and bread, the same lectures were repeated. "And you don't want people to know you're looking at them either!"

Over a cup of afternoon coffee he was issued a notebook, pens, pencils, and a bag to carry them. He looked at a photograph on the wall; Roosevelt's smiling face had been replaced.

At 2:30 he was issued a .38 caliber pistol and holster. The sergeant called it a ".38 detective special." Wally told him he was familiar with how to use a .38 revolver, but not under what circumstances it might be needed. As the sergeant showed him how to wear the firearm on his belt, he discussed unfortunate situations where he might need protection in an informal yet purposeful way. "Y'know, it's entirely possible you could hit an 'it's-either-you-or-me' type situation."

Just before heading to Mess for dinner, a confidential list of likely locals' names that he probably would need to confront was shared. "We don't carry these lists around with us when we're on the street."

By 9:30 he was ready to sleep, mulling all the advice—all the trust—all the responsibility. Sleep triumphed.

————

On day #3 immediately after breakfast-as-usual, his verbalized orders were to report to a specific rural area in Region III, a small town called Usingen between one and two hours away from Frankfurt. He was issued an old jeep for transportation. Olive green American jeeps were fairly common on the roads no matter where one traveled. "You'll fit in just fine, Rothwell." No one used his rank in conversation.

In retrospect, his transition to this assignment was accomplished rather quickly as if there were impending issues of consequence. Yet, there was remarkably little actual training per se, the colonel invested a lot of his time on the logic of what needed to be done. Young Wally fit the colonel's anticipated human template well. "You look the part" he said raising his eyebrows as a gesture to express confidence, "you'll do fine."

At first he wondered if this community had been selected since he was such an untrained novice. In other words, it was a remote place for newbie Private Rothwell to learn the trade at fairly low initial risk. After abbreviated descriptions of Usingen, no one expressed any particular interest in the strategic value of what appeared an inconsequential town—just one more place to be checked off a master list somewhere. "It's a pretty little town, I think you'll like living there" said another private at breakfast.

Wally studied some area maps since he had to familiarize himself with local placenames.

As he was driving to his new assignment, now by himself, he felt empowered by his knowledge and his ability to speak like a local. But, he felt vulnerable or at least ill-equipped to produce any results described by the colonel. Still, his built-up confidence was now carrying him. He was on a mission!

The only thing of any potential interest in little Usingen

was a small old regional hospital serving a couple dozen elderly folks, some sick patients, and a small group of wounded military. It was a well-shaded, comfortable-looking place with empty chairs out front where residents might sit later on in the spring. It looked more nursing home than hospital.

As evening set in, signs of impending winter lingered in the air as he walked around the village curiously implanting routes in his head. There were few lights and even fewer residents walking around. Though impossible to get lost here, he was educating himself on his new environment and too exhausted to do much else.

He checked in. His new home was on the second floor of a small hotel with a bathroom down the hall. It was so quiet there was no reason to fear anyone or anything. It took ten minutes to unpack, five to undress and get into bed, two more to fall asleep.

7

Wally saw firsthand how the countryside had devolved during what was now being called the Second World War to distinguish it from devastations of twenty-five years before. When an observer sees what armed conflict produces, it creates a never-again sentimentality pervading the spirit of most. But there were different kinds of lingering spirits. For example, some felt subjugated unjustly, some self-righteously defended beliefs that were no longer predominant, and some felt finally liberated. But most were cautious about opinions, sharing private emotions only with trusted friends and family.

In fact, private matters were deliberately shielded because everyone was awkwardly sensitive to who might be listening or passing judgment on their behavior as the war clouds wafted away into passive sunsets. It was different than the Switzerland he knew well.

He learned postwar feelings throughout Germany retained active pockets of pan-German fanatics and diehard Third Reich loyalists—even lingering anti-Semitism and Hitler adoration.

So, to start, he took the "automatic arrest list," and zeroed in on the "usual suspects." Because local village officials and political appointees had sworn loyalty to the Third Reich, they grabbed the CIC's first attentions. The proactive process to round up these particular subjects was already underway.

One at a time, easy targets were apprehended without fanfare and sent away.

But his job became more subtle.

As Private Rothwell interpreted his assignment, the overriding purpose was to uncover lingering Nazis and determine levels of allegiance. The specific job was to arrest those who proclaimed (or who had proclaimed in the past) any sort of Nazi faithfulness. These were sought without making himself look American or conspicuous.

One of the first things he decided to do was to establish a working informant network. These were casual, private relationships carefully selected to yield productive dialogues. It could be rumors, neighborhood gossip, or any other didja-hear-about type chatter or even real news. It was about socializing, accumulating information, and learning—it was about learning the local lingo, gossips, "did-ja-hear-about" gab sessions—it was about being inconspicuously added to the town's membership of "he's-okay" guys.

Within weeks, he figured things out because he pondered every detail. When alone under the café's umbrella, he would unknowingly tap the ends of his fingers together in confidence, making hand-steeples between sips of strong coffee. When he made notes to himself, words were penned discreetly. Then later before going to bed he would connect dots, place question marks next to names, or draw arrows where associations became of interest. The next day, he'd repeat the processes unassumingly around town in different places ...with his usual infectious broad smiles.

———

During this time, one unexpected informant, a well-weathered old Communist who had recently been released from a Nazi concentration camp, chitchatted with him about some patients at the nearby German Army hospital. In his curmudgeonly but believable old-man charm, Ludwig alleged with some "who-cares?" abandon that these patients served dual purposes. "Those guys aren't *that* sick!"

"That's one way to look at it." Wally engaged.

"Recovering soldiers?" Ludwig speculated. "...maybe, but more likely a cover for those SS and probably other damned Nazis as well ...in *my* opinion."

SS "players" remained pocketed throughout West Germany. With this withered fellow, it may have or may not have been a secret what Wally's job was, but it indeed marked the point when Private Rothwell began building his next plan of action—a plan he crafted carefully.

The acronym "SS" stood for Schutz-Staffel (Schutzstaffel), for protection squadron or defense corps. Under Hitler, it became a major paramilitary organization for the Nazi Party. Beginning 1920 as a volunteer unit providing security at Nazi Party meetings under Heinrich Himmler's leadership (1929–45), it grew from a tiny group to one of the most powerful coalitions in the Third Reich. Built on Nazi ideology, the SS was responsible for many crimes against humanity, and ultimately banned by the end of the war.

Notebook pages filled with more of Ludwig's remarks, mostly unproductive.

He remembered faces. The U.S. Army's covert investigation in Usingen commenced quietly, organized by this young army private—a newbie intelligence agent, who was figuring out how to handle this kind of lead. He didn't want to overreact.

Could that informant be trusted? How would he get anyone else to identify specifically which patients this informant was referring to? How many were there? Why would anyone disclose information to him anyhow? Was it chatter? Or, evidence? He asked around.

There was Anna and Wilhelm, dead-end streets. Helga had lots of opinions about everybody else but mostly sympathy for the hospital residents.

Sociable Wally started engaging in regular relaxed

conversations with everyone at the hospital from janitors to nurses to doctors. People got used to seeing him walking about along with other volunteers, visitors and family. He exchanged smiles with every resident, and they identified him as a friendly guy to have around, not anyone to fear.

But, he recognized similarities among a few hospital residents—a certain few who just didn't exactly fit. With a keen sense of grasping subtle German innuendo and slang, he distinguished several peculiar verbal inconsistencies that seemed odd for this part of the country. Wally's ear for linguistic nuances kicked in.

He began an inventory of the likely-liable.

But the clincher struck him one day when he realized that this group of patients did not have any uniforms!

Unlike hospital staff who didn't notice it at all, Wally knew all SS military had to destroy their uniforms immediately after the war. Regular soldiers did not. Therefore, the recovering soldiers who had kept their uniforms were ruled out as he pondered the probable meaning of missing uniforms. He paid attention to this divergent cluster of patients.

He learned their names.

Were they a little too friendly with each other? Or, was that just imagination? After all, hospitals are lonely places. Didn't they seem to be cleverly excluding other German army personnel from routine banters? Or, was that just because they knew each other better?

Could they be SS?

He became wary about how next to play his cards.

Private Rothwell listened for telltale inferences in speech and mannerisms. References to certain locations and events cropped up, but with signs suggesting involvement in something unseemly in ever-so-subtle ways.

Comparing this group with others in beds nearby, he noted inconsistencies among those who supposedly served together but who now had different recollections of the same event.

Then he noticed these particular guys using certain military words and phrases that probably were more SS-oriented, something any other American wouldn't likely detect. For example, there was something just not right about references to their chain of command. While they may have mutually agreed not to use SS phraseology to avoid detection, Wally did discern telltale inferences.

Having been educated in Switzerland, Wally's spoken language was "high German" and, when used, made him appear educated or perhaps raised in a well-placed family (though "Italian" on stage, his mother only used "high German" at home). His language gift, however, was his ability to shift word choices and pronunciation to various dialects and to less formal "low German" without thought—vernacular he had acquired in high school in Trogen. This was an on-the-street asset he used to gain social confidences no matter what the venue.

Poker-faced Wally was studious about gaining accurate information. He meticulously turned suppositions into conclusions without revealing motives for his curiosities. Within a couple months, upon scrutiny and shrewd investigative techniques, he identified thirteen recovering "patients," a few of whom were getting ready for discharge.

All thirteen were finally arrested with the help of a constabulary unit because there were so many—more than Private Rothwell could handle by himself and more than his colonel could ever have imagined.

Among those arrested were a few SS officers, including one Nazi general, one high-level Gestapo agent, and one Nazi loyalist government official. Eventually all were sent to a regional jail.

This turned out a big deal!

The experience was achieved by combining common sense and clever patience. As a result of this particularly effective and now noticed operation, Private Rothwell was recognized by all the in-charge officers. He progressed to the top of the field list at CIC headquarters. It became a celebrated event, like kicking the field goal that won the game.

Private Rothwell was promoted to corporal (as well as issued a series of three-day passes) during this otherwise mild winter. He now had in-house name recognition.

Yes, it did turn out to be a big deal for boosting American

intelligence in southern Germany, one of the bigger "finds."

———

While ideologists did remain here and there and numerous further arrests accomplished, it didn't take very long before longstanding radical Nazi-oriented political sentiments began disappearing. Nazi extremism was fading.

The now old National Socialist Germany had been imploding during that mild 1945-46 winter, confirming its looming demise witnessed around the world. It was more like a slow cremation instead of just a burial—embers lingered. But it was eventually abandoned for something more substantial and pervasive than the Nazi smoke trail left behind.

New winds were blowing as those fumes of war were dissipating.

From this new more industrially predisposed midwife, modern postwar Germany was conceived and reborn. The process of thriving amid healthy commercial development was beginning to take hold as the cleansing of its dirty smoke-laden skin continued. This process was imperative for the world to witness.

The Nuremberg trials had commenced—a conspicuous forum where primary Nazi masterminds were tried for war crimes. Industry created new jobs. People relocated. The U.S. remained distinctly present to assure an appropriate rebirth of the country. Healthy commerce had begun to thrive.

Meanwhile, the term "Iron Curtain" resurrected inside speeches and newspapers to illustrate how the north-south border from Finland to Greece had become a hard demarcation line between two ideologies—a border cutting Germany in half. The island of Berlin, east of the Iron Curtain, was also divided into two parts spawning what came to be known as the Berlin Wall.

———

Meanwhile, efforts to accelerate covert reconnaissance inside communist activities in Germany were being accelerated by the Americans. The communists appeared to be shifting management out of Frankfurt for some unknown reason. Communist infiltrators were transmitting information to the Soviet Union right alongside American infiltrators doing exactly the same thing in reverse. Priorities changed daily despite an obvious calmness pervading the 970th's headquarters.

An interesting conundrum surfaced: Wally hadn't yet received any sort of security clearance; his access to privileged intel was achieved by exception. He hadn't received in-depth instruction about other groups' operations, about his CIC group's overriding tactical purpose, or virtually anything else about investigative strategies or intelligence community culture. Such omissions had to be fixed.

Corporal Rothwell's job was about to take on yet further twists.

8

Attitudes regarding Wally's natural knack for on-the-street knowhow gave him attention from the colonel, of course. As corporal and newbie, deference evolved into admiration from other "green and pinks" in the room as well. Gaining modest panache for thinking like a German and deciphering cultural innuendoes, his value as well as his self-esteem elevated several notches.

Once this inherent astuteness for counter intelligence had been recognized, he simply had to be formally educated per established military protocols. With little doubt about innate abilities, he didn't possess any specialized training or have course certifications—necessary credentials when considering future assignments. Without any holdups hindering approvals, his next orders would enroll him into specialized training during the spring of 1946 at Fort Holabird, an army base in Maryland.

Considering his work record, it had apparently become awkward to explain how he had never received any formal training at all. Plus, there was a great deal of urgency in the air even though there was no war.

———

Fort Holabird was near Baltimore. Prior to World War II, it was both an ordnance depot and research center for military vehicle development. The now-famous jeeps had been originally tested and refined for use by the army at this location. However, that part of this base was set aside for the U.S. Army Intelligence School was *not* common knowledge.

With a days' notice to pack up and thirty minutes' notice to board the jeep, in less than two more hours he was dropped at the airfield, first leg on his way west.

Among stacks of boxes, he found himself sitting on a crate in the loading bay—spirit waiting, mind wondering, mood wandering. Nervous pensiveness competed with needed patience. The tiny waiting room was jammed with workers and other military heading west—soldiers milling around, gabbing, or reading books as if it were a real airline terminal. These smiling soldiers were heading home. The usually sociable Wally felt alone, invisible.

All night trans-Atlantic plane ride to Baltimore were exhausting. Meditating about how National Socialism was crumbling but how communism was taking its place as a divergent alternative, he subconsciously embraced the West's role, the U.S. Army's role, and what role Corporal Walter Rothwell might have to play. Feeling odd man out, he just didn't know how he could fit into the army's official stewpot of competing oil and water-type ingredients.

The prop plane pitched and bounced, ricocheting off thick clouds as the propellers' unrelenting whine prohibited sleep. He thought about geography, about time zones, about how long this never-ending night was going to last. Dozing was interrupted by muscle reflexes or shoulders shifting sideways from the oversized sound-asleep guy next to him.

———

Germany's newly formed boundaries were being further sculpted into something different and unintended. While British, French, and American occupational zones congealed together into what would become West Germany, Soviets advanced different priorities and aligned to the east into what became the German Democratic Republic (or GDR, or East Germany).

Complicating matters, Berlin's correspondingly governed four zones aligned similarly creating an island for the West to administer completely inside Soviet-managed East Germany.

The term Soviet refers to the U.S.S.R. or Union of Soviet Socialist Republics. Though comprised of fifteen lesser countries and Russia, this association was governed from Moscow. It reflected a Marxist-Leninist philosophy—a committed pro-Russian political view during World War II and afterwards for more than forty five years until it was dissolved in 1991.

———

The plane lifted, listed, lurched and continued to forbid sleep.

Deliberating shifting responsibilities he wondered if that black holster would again be needed?

He couldn't see anything out his window.

Seeking wayward Nazis had been swiftly replaced by new goals penetrating the undercurrents of communist-oriented restiveness. Allies just a dozen months before, Soviets were now political adversaries—were they our enemy?

The plane rolled, tossed, and yawed. Sleep wasn't going to happen even though he closed his eyes. "Wasn't the war over?" he found himself whispering to himself.

He wasn't an army trooper digging foxholes; he was more like a policeman!

No, not a cop or a badge wearer, more like a detective! He wasn't Hollywood's John Wayne; he felt more like Agatha Christie's Hercule Poirot, maybe Sherlock Holmes—a sleuth with stealthy eyes on one hand, coupled with the ability to speak like Perry Mason behind closed doors using any European language they chose to use.

Walking tall in daydreams, Corporal Walter Rothwell Jr. was thriving through unknowns and this self-image ...convinced a mere gumshoe he was not!

Dawn emerged behind the reeling aircraft.

Before landing, Wally actually dozed with closed eyes contemplating just how one identifies "international evidence" or assigns guilt inside "international courts." In the end, whose rules apply?

———

Landing at first light, it was the first time Wally actually experienced the United States that he could remember—an event he wasn't really able to share with anyone!

Though born in California, he could recall nothing having abandoned his birthplace at such a young age. Everything he looked at was part of an almost foreign culture—yet it was his own!

Two stripes now on his upper sleeves, he walked purposefully to where transportation at Fort Holabird had been arranged. No evidence of war *here*! He stared out the windshield at the utter routineness embodied by this good-sized city, Baltimore—eyeballing what stores and houses actually looked like in America. He found himself ogling repetitiousness of military buildings once on base.

Uniforms and green jeeps made him comfortable.

After greetings from crisply dressed soldiers with well-shined shoes, he noted how everything was clean and orderly. Soldiers saluted regularly. Formations of ten or twenty troops marched by rhythmically. The word "sir" was used conspicuously, and accentuated.

Jeeps were shiny green, even tires were slick black.

U.S. flags whipped audible snaps in the breeze.

His classroom was in session the next day with Corporal Rothwell present and accounted for.

Needless to say, this eight week course of by-the-book CIC

training probably did not expand his knowledge much beyond what he already knew.

He recounted stories in class as on-the-ground examples of military intelligence. Corporal Rothwell gained the appropriate MOS (military occupational specialty) so he could officially continue working this specialty.

Wally was now investing more than just time into new education. Military intelligence and strategies, as class subjects, were taking the place of law school. Counter intelligence was becoming a new major. His cool, problematical questions probed deeper and deeper into the intricacies of the discipline—this narrow, private, and so consequential domain.

As he thought about the college-esque environment, he recalled the piano, and how people would ask him to play those boogie-woogie tunes over and over again. Emerging from jazzy black keys on that old piano would be his friends' questions about how he did it. He never could explain exactly how it came naturally through his fingers.

But in class, people were listening to *his words* asking *his* opinion about news developments, about political decisions, about problem resolutions, not to mention all those oblique "what-if" questions that inescapably stalked every meeting. He took them with astute vigor, humor, and effective reasoning—not overlooking a good stage presence his mother had taught him years before. The "what" was always easier to explain than the "how" especially if you could smile like he could.

And, here he was, *only* a corporal!

After gaining the formal MOS, he promptly exchanged a student's chair for the podium in the very same classroom serving an instructor at that school at Fort Holabird. Classrooms were always full.

In a few weeks he was subsequently promoted to warrant officer, junior grade. Warrant officers are officers typically promoted from enlisted soldiers and rank between the highest enlisted grade (E-9) and the lowest officer grade (O-1).

As instructor, he taught two specialties: interrogation techniques, and managing informants.

Warrant Officer Rothwell, at age 23, was earning respect

WES CHOC

inside and outside the classroom.

———

As busy as he was, he did find time to examine at least a few threads of America, a country he hardly knew except by references from school, family, and stories told by others in uniform. But he never had many opportunities to get much on-the-ground sense for this at-peace place.

He was American in birth, spirit, passport; but not in experience.

Even though he didn't get to New York or Philadelphia, one thing he did do was watch three Orioles baseball games from the stands eating hotdogs, popcorn, and yelling at umpires. He even attended two concerts before the end of this multi-month tour of duty listening to well-groomed symphonic strings, then some well-tuned jazzy reverberations.

Only once did Wally leave Baltimore, to take a quick trip to Washington, D.C. for a Pentagon meeting. Though able to see the capitol building and some monuments at a distance through the windshield, there was no time for any capital sightseeing. Symbols of America were nonetheless piercing a new tattoo …inside his chest, a branding no one else could actually see.

———

At work, desks were side by side in the back room. When not in the classroom he was assigned one of the half dozen desks set aside for instructors. Because of extra chairs and how close the desks were to each other, it was tricky walking through without zigzagging and bumping into people and other things.

He had regular conversations with other instructors and staff. One of these was Henry Kissinger (two desks away) who, also at 23 years of age (born the same month, same year as Wally only twelve days apart) had been teaching military officers for a couple months before Wally joined the staff.

54

Born in Bavaria, Henry was extraordinarily well-informed about intricacies of political parties, German history, and Nazi methodologies. Being Jewish, he and his parents fled Nazi persecution and moved to New York (via London) in 1938. After being drafted, because of the shortage of German speakers and Henry's own résumé, his career into the CIC was rapid and in many ways parallel to Wally's own at the time.

Even at their rather young ages among instructors, Kissinger was deemed expert in international affairs, and Rothwell was considered an authority in matters of counter intelligence.

Classroom sessions were intense. Commanders gave frequent briefings on why pressures were so unpredictable in Germany despite reconstruction. Parenthetical remarks by Henry or Wally were added during and after class inside little conclaves of interested participants. Most U.S. student soldiers were naïve about communism and why it had become so important in politics. This is why verbal footnotes from CIC's colonel were frequently added to elevate the importance of the staff's work these get-togethers.

Both Wally and Henry were fluent in German, but speaking English was required. Even so, Henry had such a profoundly heavy accent he couldn't manage verbal interactions well, so using English was challenging (almost embarrassing) for him. Such communication idiosyncrasies obviously ear-catching, were eye-catching as well to those listening because Henry relished talking in front of others. Thriving on attentions received, he liked to ask himself questions that only he could then answer. No question from the soldiers was ever too hard.

But these self-consciousness guttural pronunciations had bothered Henry ever since he'd been around English speakers, so he sought opportunities to improve his accent privately whenever he could. This is why Wally turned out to be so useful to Henry that summer. They spent time over coffee voicing certain words and phrases over and over so Henry could gain better enunciation.

While such chats were honest practice sessions, Wally also listened to Henry's opinions about Soviet Russia's involvement in the war, and how there were likely to be consequences to deal with. Privately, however, there was little other socialization.

Henry Kissinger was not famous in 1946, of course; but,

Henry did go on to play consequential roles as American diplomat and political scientist for decades. As time went on, Wally always would notice how Henry's professorial techniques became conspicuously newsworthy during the 1950s and 60s.

By mid-summer 1946, Wally was promoted yet again, this time to second lieutenant. Where he was physically located, however, no salutes acknowledged officers like everywhere else in the army. The word "sir" wasn't even used. As much as his job was ranking up, it was as if nothing had changed at all.

Returning to West Germany late that summer, Kissinger headed for Camp King on the outskirts of Oberusel, Taunus. During the War, Camp King was the interrogation center for the German Air Force.

Meanwhile, Wally continued his job instructing classes at the Fort. He knew he was going to be assigned to a European post eventually and soon. It could be any day whether finished with his role as instructor or not.

As soldiers commiserated among all but the highest ranks, reassignments were seldom made more than a couple days in advance. There were jokes about having to pack, unpack, and repack one's duffel being one's primary responsibility. So, it was a prize for anyone who got five days' or more notice. Nevertheless, in August his crystal ball suggested he'd be gone by the end of September—his turn was obviously coming up.

Newspaper media headlined updates for public consumption. Features described side effects from massive German migration out of lands that had become part of Poland or the Soviet Union as well as German-occupied Sudetenland in Czechoslovakia. By 1950 about 12-14 million Germans had fled or were expelled from east-central Europe into areas that would become postwar West Germany and Allied-occupied Austria.

Most of these migrants came from areas ceded to Poland and the USSR (7 million) and from Czechoslovakia (3 million). These were the largest of all postwar expulsions from Central and

Eastern Europe that in the end displaced over 20 million people in all. It often seemed the hordes of survivors moving from one place to another outnumbered the longer term residents already there.

But there were many justifications for population movements. Comingling of so many politically motivated events had been variously described as community transfers, or ethnic cleansing, even genocide …all depending upon what precisely you might have been reading or who you were listening to. Indefensible information was commonly labeled trustworthy.

This was the backdrop for daily briefings covering divergent areas of interest. Certain news coupled with observations from unnamed sources here and there, were scrutinized in detail with a variety of implications—each possibility having two or three or more conceivable outcomes.

Actual names of sources were never revealed, only numbers instead. Sometimes, a placename would be applied to categorize parallel events. Untrustworthy sources were scale-rated as to their high or low reliability or past value inside the context of these second-hand reports relayed from Frankfurt.

Then there were explicit for-their-ears-only updates describing American troop withdrawals, repositions, imminent base closures, or high-level interrogations and ongoing legal trials coming out of Europe. There were base-oriented details about army comings and goings, introductions, and missions. A day wouldn't be complete without a story or two about what certain agents had heard (using placenames to categorize them) and anecdotal conclusions for others' benefit.

At one of these meetings, Lieutenant Rothwell learned how the army had been reestablishing a hush-hush intelligence venture near Frankfurt—a backroom operation more covert than even the CIC was to most people.

The colonel in charge of the CIC kept eyeing the new lieutenant without expressing any specific point. Wally couldn't help feeling he was being singled out for something more far-reaching than teaching novices how-to techniques or for rounding up wayward Nazis.

Wally didn't quite make it to the end of his eight week teaching stint.

9

With avid postwar mission-shifting from Nazism to Communism going on inside the intelligence community, in September 1946 Lt. Rothwell was assigned to the 970th CIC Group in Europe. Its headquarters was at the same base near Frankfurt, Germany, he'd served out of previously. Since it wasn't likely he'd be doing the same sort of small town work, all he could do was speculate.

Actually, he still didn't really know precisely what he'd be doing at all.

The flight back to Frankfurt was uneventful, the air smooth. Although he was losing hours while the plane to'd and fro'd over time zones, he slept contentedly amid high-pitched engine buzzes and whines. He awoke in time to absorb from the sky how early autumn's green landscapes faded into orangey yellow. As the transport plane rhythmically lost altitude, the iconic canvas massaged his eyes.

The propeller-driven craft descended over the Low Countries and eastern France. When the plane began banking left then right, he caught sight of the Rhine Valley and eventually urban stretches approaching Frankfurt.

Once landed, he was dutifully escorted to the CIC. In Frankfurt, the 970th was headquartered in the abandoned I.G. Farben buildings which the U.S. had used during the war. It even looked American despite its German setting. Within the hour, he was transferred to another tired green, war-weathered jeep for transport to Bad Nauheim. The army sergeant driver didn't talk much which suited Wally's mood.

Sensations of comfort permeated his physical and mental being as the jeep sped along zigzagging over village streets and through countryside. Like being wrapped in a flannel blanket, he felt warm contentment reading store names in German, recollecting placenames from mileage signs, seeing common European architecture—a contented serenity being back around accustomed settings.

He was smiling to himself. He was ready, willing, and able to take on this assignment, no matter what it was, no matter where it was …no matter who noticed him or not.

Handshakes were followed by coffee, and casual updating about recent changes to their functions at the Sub Region offices here in Bad Nauheim. They talked about food, road construction, and all those newfangled typewriters back at CIC Headquarters in suburban Frankfurt about twenty some odd miles away.

There were three groups in this outlying resort area totaling less than fifty soldiers. He learned he had been assigned to the group specializing in matters of direct on-the-ground intelligence in southern Germany. His first impressions were that this might be no more than episode two of another Usingen-type operation.

Other nearby groups specialized in things like refugee screening, cross-border espionage, and interrogation including occasional episodes of serious persuasion among unforthcoming but suspicious locals.

Though physically positioned near each other, staff didn't enter into conversations about specific projects, people, or problems with any other group—very little socialization with each other either for that matter—nor even a piano to keep fingers nimble.

The office count in Wally's group was never more than 15-18 along with 3-4 civilian volunteer admin staff. They convened daily operations discreetly inside a few small buildings all part of this mountainside resort no more than an hour east of Frankfurt. But it didn't take long for in-charge ranking commanders to get down to business. Though rank wasn't displayed by uniform (everyone wore those green and pinks), it was definitely determined by speech and deference.

The CIC's underlying mission had been redefined to changing circumstances. A few months ago, the emphasis was eliminating leftover Nazi loyalists while neutralizing in-place Nazi functions and infrastructures. Though these efforts remained nominally, the revised mission redefined the we's and they's.

CIC's new agenda was divided into two parts.

- What: Understand intentions and motives of the Communist Party in West Germany and analyze their intentions and activities.

- How: Infiltrate West German Communist Party (headquartered near Frankfurt at the time) and solicit information not be readily obtainable from usual sources.

Focus points were underscored with those same repetitious words "highly classified."

Wally found some words puzzling. Explaining precisely what was and what wasn't considered "highly classified" versus what might be merely "secret" or "confidential" wasn't exactly clear nor explained. But, the CIC colonel didn't use "secret" much at all. An emphasized "very" preceded adjectives describing just about everything they talked about with deliberate pauses before and after whenever such words were uttered.

Moods in the room were thick, tired, heavy.

Questions were sometimes left unanswered. Events were mazes to navigate.

The Army had considerable interest in what certain communist-oriented groups were doing in West Germany. Well-known names, the kind one might later read about in newspapers or *Time* magazine, were cited offhandedly. The commander's tightlipped descriptions about unpublished objectives assigned to national figures were woven into most reports. Comments like "whatever *that* means" or "how would *he* know" peppered the Q&A sessions that followed. Nevertheless, everyone took the information seriously.

It didn't take long for Wally to understand yet another language—words used to infer more than just one thing—words only used inside this inner sanctum of military intelligence board rooms.

For example, one of these words was "research." Whenever it was written on orders or in logs, or as an explanation for how time was spent, it really signified covert activity in the field.

Actual activities were never described using everyday words on papers read by other army departments or by anyone else up the chain of command. Such "highly classified" documents used this private jargon so everyone who needed to know, knew.

Consequently, "highly classified" introduced beginnings and endings of every meeting. Those in the room were regularly questioned if they understood what these words meant. Prompt interest was sustained as the silhouette of this new adversary, communism, took tangible form.

A vacuum of good intelligence existed since there were too few authentic German interrogators among staff. Though many staff spoke the language fluently, few could speak it in a way that native-born residents could—locals could always tell who was "foreign" and who was *one of them.*

Foreigners, mind you, were treated with respect; after all, locals did recognize occupiers and governments were changing things all around them. But, respect and trust were two different things. For this reason, Lieutenant Rothwell was capturing center stage as one who would be playing a key role.

Though no formal classrooms, daily briefings disclosed communist-oriented idiosyncrasies from details collected by traditional methods in the field. Fresh intelligence was presented amid supposition and speculation then discussed, debated, and often discarded. It became evident there was too little if any candid on-the-street raw intelligence they really needed. Inferences from local German informants were translated and decoded in a variety of ways—ways that suggested no one was really sure.

Wally's job was being invented right in front of him.

Once again he was to burrow into the city's underbelly engaging informants at local, regional or even top levels if possible—to mine information from this crude rock-solid terrain. Again, his social skills, combined with an eye for inconsistences, were needed to bring in a new load of raw data—those veins of barely visible evidential gold that only he could unearth in this part of West Germany.

Wally was morphing from being that poster-pictured khaki-colored yellow-barred officer into an infiltrator, snooper, and undercover detective.

In a couple of weeks he attended an in-depth "intelligence research training" program where even more sophisticated interrogation techniques were explained and demonstrated.

His just-pressed, army-pleated, collar-barred khakis hung unused in his closet. At the office he wore pink and greens like everyone else. But on the street, he cinched a fancier belt on his newer more casual non-uniform as he began to shovel his way underground into the mud and dust of daily life.

Alone, isolated, he asked himself "where might this lead? Will anyone know I'm there?"

10

Meanwhile, as Wally learned as much as he could about what communism was up to in West Germany, he also adjusted to daily routines, new people around him, and this new, more urban living style. There were jeeps and trucks everywhere. No bombs were exploding anymore, but there was a great deal of activity nonetheless in the months and years following the war.

There was more military around him, even more American civilians doing postwar work. He easily recognized who they were even though those who didn't know him probably thought he was just another out-of-work German.

However, locals always spotted Americans by their behavior, their speech, their faces. True, some American faces could pass as European—until they opened their mouth, that is.

There was little doubt English-speakers were in charge.

Wally had become respected by both peer personnel and commanding officers. One of the new clerical staff, Thelma, caught his eye from day one. Every opportunity he had, he tried to catch hers as well.

Thelma recognized these types of squints and glimpses, and was judicious about glancing back at all these younger and older men wandering around the building's tight quarters. More than one eye looked her way. The mystery behind being so demur stirred more than one heart. She didn't reciprocate in kind, but once in a while her eyes would linger back for one extra second— just long enough to be ever-so-slightly inviting.

Wally thrived on these one-extra-second eyelash twinks.

———

By now, Lieutenant Rothwell was a higher ranking investigating officer, and had his own private secretary; her name was Marti, an American of Swiss heritage.

She too was multilingual, educated, and skilled at discreet report composition and data analysis. A woman now in her 40s, Marti may not have been as popular with the others as Thelma, but she was a darned good analyst. Acting more like a team member, most grew to respect her for her undercover insights that aligned neatly next to her desktop skills. So, because of heritage and language abilities, she fit into this group and made Wally's desktop duties easier.

Clerical staff was hard to find. When required, soldiers with sufficient administrative skills filled voids; but, with tactical shifts from Germany to Japan, recruiting North Americans for these European jobs became the solution. Those who came were paid-volunteers who agreed to come overseas to help with postwar efforts. Without the bombs, it was also a chance to travel at very little cost for those more daring, like Thelma and Marti.

———

Although this particular admin group in Frankfurt hired only a few volunteers, their in-baskets overflowed as typewriters clacked endlessly.

Proportionately, few women worked on these American bases at all. Those who were there were inevitably popular among soldiers—if not just for healthy in-office social contact and hometown humor, but for human distractions that twenty-something soldiers always observed and sought.

"Didja see that skirt she had on today?" was a common mutual interrogation question in the men's bathroom.

———

Wally knew what Thelma's job was of course. She used the stenograph, acted as court reporter, took shorthand at breakneck speed, and typed faster than she could take shorthand—at least that's what everyone said. Besides, everyone spent an extra ten to sixty seconds at her desk whenever they passed by (to verify these speeds for later analysis?).

Thelma didn't notice, or pretended not to notice. She knew how to raise her face to acknowledge those hovering while keeping her eyes focused on her typing. No matter how accurate her work may have been, she was repeatedly asked to verify something she had just typed.

But what was it? Was it her natural efficiencies behind the desk? Or was it her slightly curled hair and how it fell over her shoulder? Her taunting eyes?

Thelma wasn't new to the army. She had just been reassigned to Sub Region #3, to a top-rung civilian job here at Bad Nauheim. Working for the boss had prestige as well as privilege. Thelma had experience working in another field technical unit near Frankfurt doing similar work.

But what was it? Was it her choice of clothes? Or, was it the way she walked?

Among civilians, Thelma had rank. Among army officers, she was the very attractive Canadian who everyone talked about behind her back.

Everyone noticed Thelma.

So, there was a great deal of competition for Thelma's attention in particular among both young bucks as well as those tenured with graying temples.

In a matter of weeks, Wally made sure he caught Thelma's eye a lot more often than anyone else—leading to coffees after lunch—then to helping her with her winter coat when she left the building—plus those accidental collisions as they zigzagged around desks and chairs. It didn't take long for her smiles to begin anticipating Wally's eyes.

One time, he asked her where she was from. Everyone knew she was Canadian, but this was one good conversation starter he hadn't used before.

"Oh, I'm from western Canada …Saskatchewan, know where that is?" she asked with a friendly smile. Saskatchewan was a placename everyone knew, but no one knew much of anything about this middle-Canada province. So her eyebrows lifted with some surprise when Wally answered her query with a smile.

"o'course, I do." Wally then returned her lifted eyebrows with a copy-cat version of his own; it clicked.

"Well, if you do, then the only place you've probably ever heard of is Regina. Well I'm from a little rural community called Marquis, kind of near Moose Jaw. And, yeah, I've seen moose, not many jaws though." Thelma's humorous sarcasm baited Wally into further dialogue about where each of them had once lived, travels, and mutual interests throughout Europe.

One topic led to another, then another. He memorized details so he could ask sensible questions next time. This advanced further into a first dinner date. Anyone looking at them could detect mutual interest. A second dinner led to a third, to cafés for coffee in between, movies once a week. The conclusion of one date automatically led to planning the next.

After dinner one time, Thelma invited Wally to her place— something that required a good deal of discretion since social relationships were not blessed by the military. This was how he began to learn about her mother and sister, Thelma's audaciousness coming across the ocean, and all the peculiarities that made her different, special, attractive.

Thelma disclosed she signed up to come to Germany mainly to visit Europe. She also wanted Wally to know she had been in a serious relationship at her former military station in nearby Hoechst close to Frankfurt. Though surprised at the amount of attention she received, she was not naïve.

When a chance to move to Bad Nauheim surfaced that fall, her promotion became an opportunity to change geographical locations—a new start of sorts. She seized the moment.

Civilian women lived alone in individual apartments just a few blocks away from the military office buildings. These kinds of apartments were required for civilians connected to the army, so a certain number of them had to be appropriated for army use. Even though this action displaced several local families who then had to relocate, such relocations were rather common when the army needed such housing.

Due to her private housing situation, Wally visited Thelma frequently. Since not everyone had outside-the-office responsibilities as he did, it gave him advantage over social competitors. Just as his on-the-street covert investigations had landed him data returns, Wally took advantage of these more evocative explorations as well.

As daily routines dried up those get-to-know-you type conversation topics, it didn't take long for Wally to start probing longer term objectives. "Would you ever consider staying and living in Europe?" Or, "Are you going to make government your career?"

But such conversations quickly lengthened and became more relaxed—and reciprocal. Two hour dinners turned into four. Goodnight kisses lasted past midnight. Wally's questions became more personal. Although Wally hadn't been the only one interested in Thelma, the chemistry seemed to be bubbling up in those test tubes laced with champagne.

Wally held down a job with built-in stress and odd hours. Recognizing competition for Thelma's attention, and uncertain where responsibilities might next take him, he eventually expressed his interest for an even yet more serious relationship …more than once …more than twice …until she relented.

It wasn't surrender, mind you; it was a gracious agreement based upon each one fitting into the anticipations of the other ... the right time ...the right place.

———

An army chaplain married Wally and Thelma in January 1947 at a German Protestant church in Bad Nauheim. There were less than a hundred attending the ceremony, mostly soldiers, officers and staff, friends and friends of friends. Such events hadn't happened often, so it certainly drew a crowd.

Border-crossings were rather challenging to accommodate. On such short notice, no one could attend from either Wally's or Thelma's family. However, it wasn't long before the newlyweds gained permission to cross south, traveling from Germany to where Wally's mother was living in Zurich, Switzerland.

Smiles abounded. During several rounds of tea, Elizabeth asked the proverbial question to her new daughter-in-law about where she was from. A similar Thelma-esque response surfaced just like it had with Wally months before.

"Moose Jaw? Really?" Elizabeth's face widened into her beautiful stage smile as memories from floodlights twenty-five years past captured her expression. As dreamy eyes gazed up at the tin metal ceiling, one could imagine glaring stage reflections and paused recollections. "I remember Moose Jaw! Such a very tiny theater! So many steps to my changing room! Oh my!" shaking her head in smiling disbelief then closing her eyes as remembrances captured her soul.

"You've actually been there? At the theater?" Thelma's eyes asked in sync with a stunned and startled voice. Even Wally's eyebrows raised an inch.

"Why yes, I have. On my western tour, I sang classical compositions in several Canadian cities; Moose Jaw was one of these. It was a lovely event even though a small town. There was still a nice-sized audience and several encores." Elizabeth's eyes were blurring wet. "But what I remember most was the applause. You see, when you're able to hear those palms actually smack so crisply, it's a different sound when you're that close—just a few feet away." She looked into her own palms then spread her arms wide in a gracious gesture recalling her role in the original event. "Those were such beautiful German and Italian masterpieces, too."

"You went to Saskatchewan?" Wally asked raising his eyebrows further. "I had no idea ...never knew that!"

They all had a good honest chuckle at this. Elizabeth described the red rose bouquet she received afterwards, and the thoughtful reception using adjectives that pleased Thelma to hear.

Wally then went on to describe in detail some of his family's relationships to operas, orchestras, and on-stage performances— including his own performance in Königsberg. Thelma described her family, how they moved around in Canada, and how the war had been perceived from a Canadian perspective. Elizabeth tenderly engaged these dialogues better than a brand new mother-in-law might have to—to Thelma's and Wally's mutual delight.

Thelma asked many more questions about music and family, and Elizabeth was gratified to tell her stories. Thelma felt welcomed. Wally experienced a newfound pride toward both.

But the Moose Jaw coincidence turned out to be pretty significant, something that solidified this new family relationship more than anything else in particular might have.

———

Considering how Wally's on-the-street persona required him inconspicuous, in-town living arrangements with Thelma became awkward by the summer of 1947.

Frieda, the woman living in the apartment right below them introduced herself to Thelma. They saw each other every day coming and going, and chatted over coffee. She was the type who'd lean out her window to say "hi" and wave until Thelma waved back. Although she may have bumped into Wally once at the door when they were moving in, Frieda probably didn't even know what Wally really looked like. Besides, he was better at smiling and being polite than engaging in unnecessary chats. In any case, Frieda and Thelma became friends.

71

One time when Thelma was coming up the front steps, she smacked into Frieda opening the front door to leave, producing several mutual I'm-sorry-type smiles and chuckles. This in turn led into one of Frieda's predictable on-the-porch dialogs about how a lot of people were moving in and out on both sides of the street. "Except for you, I don't know many neighbors anymore. There are these little trucks, empty boxes, people carrying things in and out," Frieda lamented, her eyes repetitively scanning the street. "It's just not the street it used to be."

This time as she was stepping up, Thelma rested two small sacks of groceries onto her knee, and graciously listened to Frieda's sighing German lingo. "Oh, are they heavy? Maybe I can help you." Thelma smiled an it's-not-necessary smile as Frieda carried on not missing a beat. "Did you ever meet those two Austrian women who moved in next door?" Frieda asked with raised eyebrows and a lowered jaw. "I've been trying to be friendly, like I always am, but y'know how *Austrians* feel they're better than us locals." Her double chin bobbled as she spoke just above a whisper when her eyes listed left. "I don't know why. I wonder how they acted when they lived in Vienna. I've heard so much about…"

"No, but I'm sure I will." Thelma politely let her own words overlap Frieda's with genuine smiles conceding the woman most of the space and attention she sought, but signaling she didn't really want lengthy dialogues either as she re-hugged the grocery bags.

An inquisitive sort, nosy Frieda lived alone and thrived on casual chitchatting. Leaving her last sentence uncompleted, she started over. "At least *Americans* will gab a little with you—like you do, Thelma. You're so nice!" Frieda patted Thelma's shoulder while she readjusted her bags.

Not to be confrontational, smiling Thelma ignored the point about her really being Canadian, not American. "It's always nice to see you too, Frieda."

"But, I thought you disliked Germans!" Frieda challenged her with a pursed-lip smile as Thelma now seemed ready to go inside. "I mean, Americans came…"

"Well, certain Germans, I suppose," letting her words mingle with Frieda's courteously.

"…b'but you had one over for lunch yesterday, didn't you?"

Who Frieda saw was Wally. Perhaps he looked and acted so much like one of the neighborhood Germans, Frieda thought he really was. Wally smiled when Thelma told the story. "Who do you think she thought I was? Doesn't she know you're married?" following by more chuckles.

Nevertheless, to fit in that well, especially against curious Frieda-type scrutiny, reinforced his self-imposed German role.

Now, greater discretion about where they lived became repetitive conversation topics over the next few weeks. Wally never lingered on the front porch on purpose, and his comings and goings remained discreet through August.

A change of address had to be considered more seriously.

———

By September, over-the-dinner-table conversations were peppered with comments about shifts in priority at work, or by Frieda's spending too much time drinking coffee in their kitchen, or by counting how many days it was past her usual monthly period.

Though he didn't know it at the time, the fact that he would be going undercover for real was fast approaching. On the other hand, Thelma, as part of her job, knew about the inevitability of this upcoming surreptitious agenda better than Wally did, but dutifully said nothing—if nothing else but to prove faithfulness to the overall mission.

Meanwhile, while Thelma was working in Europe, her mother had relocated to Edmonton, Alberta, to be nearer her other daughter, Thelma's younger sister.

Once Thelma's pregnancy manifested undeniably, the conundrum was on the table. Discomfort having the baby in Europe became evident over supper each night until they decided it would be better for her to return to Canada instead of bearing the child in Germany. Besides, being physically close to her mother, after all, was a useful advantage considering Wally's upcoming assignments.

Within the month, they said their interim good-byes.

———

In February 1948, daughter Danielle was born in Edmonton. Agreeing it more suitable for Thelma to stay in Alberta until Wally's assignment improved enough for the family to reunite in Germany, mother and daughter remained separate from dad for more than eighteen months.

Wally's covert assignments had indeed become complicated. Surreptitious seeds planted during that fall of 1948 yielded unusual harvests.

11

Starting back in late 1947 just after Thelma left for Canada, the CIC assigned Wally to work in urban Frankfurt so he could familiarize himself with what kinds of people lived there, where they worked, and who they talked to. At the same time, he educated himself on how locals behaved with each other, how they played and socialized, and how he could adapt inside their local culture.

Though not yet involved in any sort of intricate or consequential clandestine operation, he tuned into the sentiments of regular people. Being German in everything but passport and inner spirit, useful tidbits of authentic data became easy to acquire.

This was Wally's stage in this new theater, but playbooks didn't have already-written scripts.

If anything, some locals assumed Wally might have been one of those residual gestapo agents lingering around—if not in fact then in disposition. Then again, this was an everyday joking allegation guys had about each other anyway. "Heck, Gustav, now you're acting like Hitler's right-hand man again. You can't *always* get your way."

Still, unspoken sensitivities prevailed in both public and private rendezvous; nearly everyone observed others' behaviors and choices to some degree. Trust was fostered over time and valued among close friends. Most just wanted things to get back to normal—whatever normal might actually be.

As a whole, Germans were reinventing not only a new culture, but also their interpersonal relationships, values, and political beliefs. Until the air cleared more broadly, things were not yet stable. Reconstruction, embarrassment, pride of heritage, and guilt-ridden history created pretty heavy baggage.

Because of casualties, more women walked around than men—more mothers raising children, more women filling jobs men used to bear. Though no one really talked about it, little boys received more attentions than they would have fifteen or fifty years before.

More than one single culture was congealing. Pockets of traditional conservatism was balanced by circles of like-minded intellectuals ...or marred by extremists who sought entirely new ways to manage life or cope with adversities.

As an inadvertent adjunct to this healing process, British, French, Soviet, and American interests continued influencing the military, the media, and the masses. Though grateful on many levels, desires among work-a-day Germans lingered for outsiders just to go away. *Protection* had been replaced by *interference* in their minds. Nevertheless, despite remedies, there was one universal inspiration: *to get their country back—Germany for Germans.*

————

Impromptu scripts detailed new roles, new names, unpredictable plotlines.

By the end of 1947 Wally slipped undercover unnoticed—ignored by other military staff (except direct chain of command) and inconspicuous to other Germans. He could now connect with new acquaintances, explore, scrutinize. Friends introduced him to more new friends—all by intricate design.

In postwar Germany, how reconstruction was coming along was a common subject with frequent "didja-hear-about..." type comments—usually about friends and family who did not survive, but including stories about people on the mend, children not getting educations, homes being rebuilt, about relatives relocating from here to there, orphans and widows. Especially in urban areas, so many people did not live or shop where they used to.

Everyday living rules were being rewritten.

Those less socially-oriented were noticed, talked about. Wally had an inherent knack about how to zero in on those having something to say, or how to console or apply trust-building empathy when needed. An intense listener, he soaked up information. He thought in German, remembered bilingually.

When he looked right at them and said "tell me more," they usually did.

But his wardrobe was genuinely German. No matter what was underneath, he sported a full length dark brown leather jacket, realistic enough to emerge as an authentic young German businessman in any gathering. He slanted his rather large indeed stylish business hat to shade his forehead, tipped a little to the left side like "in-professionals" did in those days. He even walked with self-assured German struts.

Someone might say "*Oy! Mein freund!*" to Wally. Though conscious whether he himself was being watched, it usually turned out to be one of his own "*mein fruend's!*".

Nevertheless, he carefully tailored behaviors to be inconspicuous by smiling often, shopping at local stores, mastering slang expressions, drinking coffee at certain on-street cafés, and dressing just like the other twenty-something young men.

And he was good at it.

Some days were demanding with long day-to-night-to-day hours. He noticed, he reported, he was asked to notice more. It wasn't the physical labor, but more about things that logically caught his attention. When not smiling, he was introspective. There were conjectures, eye-catching debris, off-the-cuff inferences, and hard cold facts—pressing far more brain tissue than muscle. He savored the labor.

When not actually observing people, he busied himself establishing his own covert system for transferring information from others to certain others on the inside. This communication system used warning and activation word signals—like a confidential language. Key words were only used for specific actions or requests. Intended meanings could then be understood. Time invested here was not only validated by those monitoring his reports but by those like Wally who needed to use coded lingo.

While drinking coffee at those certain cafés, Wally not only acquiesced to living two lives, he was thriving.

Over these next eighteen months, CIC officers reinforced these efforts by sharing how such work was becoming more and more consequential. His built-in stealth abilities coupled with freedoms to act were compellingly motivating for Wally.

From 1948 to 1952 the West German intelligence quarry was mined thoroughly by data treasures extracted methodically. Wally engaged people in private conversations that led to disclosures of on-the-street innuendoes, unpublished news, or potential evidence that in turn pointed in another direction to explore and excavate.

Over time, these well-planned, well-guarded efforts documented multi-layered aspects of the Communist Party. They uncovered information about safe-houses, personnel assignments, some financial records, phone-tapping practices, and courier systems. Meticulously, he assembled the missing pieces in CIC's Party jigsaw puzzle.

Usually these abundant chats and banters went nowhere; only occasionally, somewhere.

This is how he met Werner in 1948. His code name was O721; but, Wally called him Werner. It was easier.

Werner was not an intellectual by any definition. A middle-aged man, he was one, however, to engage in conversation with anyone else with a smile.

As a lithe muscular clean-shaven handyman type, he sought work wherever he could find it, making himself useful to anyone paying him a little attention and maybe couple of those new Deutsche Marks. He was the go-to guy when you needed an electrician or plumber or just someone to help move furniture.

"Just call Werner." If he couldn't do something, for a pfennig he always knew someone who could.

Werner had a sense of humor. Initially conversations were casual, but Wally sought Werner's take about those moving in and moving out. Cautious at first, Werner came to realize he had something of value to share, and Wally took advantage of it. It was also awkward since he didn't want to be observed paying too much attention to Werner, at least not in too many public places.

Without much prodding, but with some coffee and baited conversations, O721 agreed to move from public cafés to more private quarters nearby—temporarily assigned rooms or apartments that kept changing. Next week it would always be someplace else.

Werner liked being useful. He became part of Wally's courier system, he provided observations, and supplied data leads. Wally provided coffee, snacks, and left a few pfennigs. Werner liked calling him Wally instead of Walter, but they never exchanged surnames; neither asked

By now Wally had explained a coded way to leave each other messages with time or place, or subsequent changes of plan. For more complicated conversations, once sighted at the designated time, Werner would then follow 25-50 feet behind Wally on the crowded sidewalk or down a side street until he saw the door Wally entered.

Wally knew how to gain access to these stashed away places, called safe-houses. They were little more than a small room. Seldom were there bathrooms or windows—just two chairs, a table, and perhaps a pitcher and two glasses for water.

Sometimes, a few data gems were collected, assembled into something new or meaningful then discreetly handed off to someone else in another location. Regularly Wally received similar scraps to follow-up on from other insiders. Sources' names were coded, ranked, and ultimately respected for the precious resource they were. It was a bit like browsing around one yard sale after another for that one item of value. If you couldn't find it, someone always knew someone who might.

"Why is the *Goldene Gans Haus* so busy on Tuesdays?" Wally asked Werner one time.

"Well that's where those two red-headed guys critique those nuisance trials going on downtown" he reflected.

"Y'don't say!" Wally responded with furrowed brows or acquiescent puckered lips then go on commiserating with Werner about polluted water, local politics, or the police in order to ferret out any further crumbs of information. Coffee always accompanied commiseration.

Before that day was out, Wally observed who came or went from the *Goldene Gans Haus* with a sense of optimistic curiosity. Patterns inevitably emerged. Notebooks filled up.

The following week Wally asked "...next time, let me know if those same two Berliners show up, would you?" with a handshake.

"I'll find out."

Wally confirmed a rendezvous location. "Next Wednesday then?"

But once the day's work was done, Wally had no one he could really talk to, no one who was a friend enough to know he was fake German. He'd head home late, wash up, hit the rack. He couldn't bring any of Thelma's letters with him. He either destroyed them, or left a few in a shoebox with some photos—a shoebox his private secretary, Marti, kept under her desk. But Wally didn't go back on base that often—maybe two or three times a week, so periods of empty thinking were frequent.

It was challenging to be an American, born in a country he hardly knew, playing this undercover role—alone, only to commiserate with a half-German self. Often getting sleep was a fidgety process. Yet each morning he'd awake pondering tidbits of information gained the day before rising then look into the mirror at whom he needed to be.

He pursed his lips and then stepped out once again ready.

———

Reaping information wasn't always regular. Going back to the "office" with no informational harvest at all was disheartening. The meaninglessness of such events was sporadically offset by tiny pebbles of intellectual gold here and there.

Yet these slivers of word-on-the-street information revealing Party intentions, or changes of plans, or certain personalities elevated to new assignments, meant good grades on Wally's own report cards. The words were nonfiction, the process was chemistry. Data carefully translated, wrought, and worked over were evaluated just as if he were still in school—like literature inside professors' test tubes.

12

There was this one-of-a-kind café tucked away downtown called Konditorei. It specialized in varieties of coffees, teas, and pastries, but one coffee in particular always caught Wally's interest; it became his first choice. Bearing an odd name, *mohrenkopf*, a German word meaning "head of a Moor," it was a tongue-in-cheek reference to an unfortunate soul in southern Spain way back in the day. It made for amusing orders by the patrons who combined the word with names of friends.

He spent hours in this low-ceilinged crowded conclave of young adults. One pastry specialty was a chocolate-covered mousse-type confection that stole affections from nearly every passerby. He ate more than a few.

This is where Wally met Hilsa. Once a farmer's daughter from the state of Hesse, she now lived in Frankfurt and became quite active in local political activities. She liked *mohrenkopfs* too.

In places like Konditorei, when busy it's common for patrons to join other coffee sippers at their tables. This in turn created opportunities to make acquaintances and is how he met

Hilsa[2]. After that, when it was crowded, it was an easy task for either to hit it off, again exchanging views about happenings d' jour.

Hilsa, a robust middle-aged sort, paid attention to whomever paid attention to her. A natural protester, her talkative style championed popular opinions about how well everyone was coming back together after the war. Communists were exhibiting reasonable approaches. They weren't really bad according to Hilsa; she knew many of them personally!

Sipping her Moor's head, "...in my opinion, there are too many *idealists* competing with those *practicalists* who want to do things like they always have. You can't figure out who's supporting whom," Hilsa said not noticing how she dripped coffee onto the table after each emphasized word. "Why aren't *pragmatists* or *realists* speaking up?"

There was always something to clarify, explain, or defend. Each sought out the other, predicted next visits, and departed with baited political questions to resume next time. She liked Wally's take on issues, and enjoyed playing an opponent's role. He liked the parrying back and forth and took both sides as well; touchés made it all fun.

From Hilsa, Wally gained inside information about Party activities and events. He learned about future campaigns with useful insights on why they were held where they were. He uncovered names, management structure, and rationales for doing or not doing activities. Hilsa was familiar with their courier system which Wally found beneficial for predicting yet other events. He was careful never to take notes in front of her, and never make himself look too interested beyond intellectual fencing matches they both enjoyed.

She didn't have particular interest in where Wally worked; but, when asked directly, he said he was a journalist as he usually did with others in coffee shops or bars. Stubborn questions would

---

[2] Hilsa wasn't her real name. Hilsa had her own "P" number that identified informants who were useful in garnering inside information. Wally gave operatives arbitrary names, like Hilsa or Werner, just to be able to talk about them.

reveal he free-lanced for a magazine as a political reporter. He even got some stuff on the radio but revealed few other details. Depth of relationships was seldom an issue. When cornered, he'd use his standard alias, Walter Hoffman; not many were interested.

Although she was little more than an active volunteer for the Party, her path crossed others who were true organizers and Party chieftains. Wally knew how to feed attentions she sought, and this is why Hilsa became a good on-again, off-again yet low-level informant for two, almost three years.

The Party had become fractured, and Hilsa described how left hands and right hands couldn't work together—maybe not even know who each other were. At times labor parties and party bosses didn't see eye to eye, and how these impasses ended up being resolved to the dismay of other insiders. She wanted him to listen. With few privileged facts stockpiled for coffee-time sparring, she inadvertently turned these touché matches into Wally's next day reports with perspectives that were accurate …without her ever guessing his underlying motives. After all, he listened when others wouldn't.

At one point, Wally's and Hilsa's *mohrenkopfs* became such regular events that guys around Wally's office chided him about why there were so many dates. Was there only one informant? Gossip expanded. Just who was this "floozie"? To quell nattering, one time Wally took an office cohort with him for coffee and introduced him to Hilsa. When the guy reported she was indeed quite middle-aged as well as extraordinarily buxom, chatter once again became respectful, and her information appreciated.

Wally's social scene grew at the Konditorei. There were always hand-waving when he walked in. He was introduced to others who introduced him to yet others. He never knew who might be valuable or for how long any one of these acquaintances might hang around. Wally faithfully recorded scraps of words and innuendo then pieced them together later to make a sentence. With two sentences he could make a conclusion.

While certainly not the only one he enjoyed probing, Hilsa's remarks remained valuable because she knew what was going on. She provided insights he wouldn't have otherwise had. Hilsa's words turned into good intel sentences. But then, there was Berta.

13

One of Wally's coffee-drinking contacts turned out to be indispensable. He prospected for shiny data scraps— pieces that outlined plans and programs of the Party. Bit by bit, these assembled into patterns that began to make thought-provoking sense when coupled with bits and pieces from other sources. Unlike Werner or Hilsa, this new contact's info over time was different, woven deeper, richer …reliably better.

And consequential.

The young woman was mystifying to Wally. She dressed in fashionable business attire, looked like a banker, acted like a lawyer—she spoke authoritatively and chose words carefully. Wally responded in kind as he carefully panned for more data nuggets. After sharing stories over coffee, these data pieces proved accurate and useful. Her status elevated among the family of informants being nurtured.

But she was in some ways cavalier with her openness. While her candor was attractive, she was not always consistent with her timelines or critiques. Or perhaps she was clever with her choices when ranting publicly. Early on Wally picked up on this, and balanced it with his own brand of clever questioning—not interrogatively, mind you, but in a friend-sensitive way that she finally recognized, and fed. They clicked.

What he took at first as scatterbrained remarks from this dignified lady, were then channeled into useful dialogues. He was nonthreatening to her, and this let the pages turn at her own speed. This is why Wally spent so much time creating an even more intricate undercover operation to protect her and preserve uninterrupted flow of this good-as-gold information. It became his full-time job as she was no flash in the pan.

As true for other informants, some wondered what such a person's real name or real function was on the "inside." In spite of skepticism about P848's connections, no one could dismiss how well she predicted certain events, however. Was she merely trading manufactured intelligence from loaded but ultimately unreliable sources? Then of course, there were dead-end streets no one could explain. Despite many contrary speculations, no doubt…everyone was listening.

In the back-office, her file was labeled "P848" in black ink. That's how she was referenced. She had no other name.

But for Wally, six decades later reminiscing about this lady, he chose to call her Berta[3] in his own mind so she had a name, not just a number—so that she was a real person, not just a manila file folder, and risk no compromise to her person or to either of their missions even to this day.

It all started in late 1947.

First, Wally's personal image was a singular thing, and had to appear authentic. It was.

To support this emerging image, he was assigned authentic German National identification cards and a German driver's license using his alias, Walter Hoffman. He rented inconspicuous places to live. He never went where Americans went. He avoided English or other languages besides the Deutsch form of low-German. He bought German-branded merchandise.

---

[3] Again, Berta is not the actual name for P848, nor is P848 the actual "P" number for this informant.

He didn't stay in one place very long either—sometimes as little as a week, sometimes maybe as long as two months. These semi-furnished apartments had everything needed for sleeping, eating and hygiene. He changed addresses often—addresses he'd never use again. He immersed into inconspicuousness so resourcefully it became a passive habit like breathing—automatic and repetitive.

Critically important: no pesky landlords or nosy neighbors.

Despite an amiable personality, he made no long-lasting friendships on purpose. For those asking questions among themselves, they probably presumed he worked in a newly created bureaucratic job—there were many of them around. Or, maybe he could be having an affair. He'd play poker, go skiing, or bowling with guys he met occasionally; or, he'd just wander in and about different places. He was open about his freelance journalism to offset deeper probes into his inquisitive behaviors—somehow newpapers' or magazines' names never surfaced. He passed introduction tests every time.

Depth of relationships was seldom an issue. Wally was just a good-natured loner.

Although he owned a complete set of army uniforms, he didn't really know where they were stored. Instead, he carried himself "mufti" (a colloquial word meaning "in civvies").

When he moved around, he used a couple of frayed leather suitcases. Though he didn't have many personal belongings or clothes, he always dressed sharp. In metaphor, he was without doubt a thoroughbred German. Such details assured unthreatening camouflage for their intended purposes.

Unresolved nonetheless, was how to explain to oneself why being so well camo'ed, so German, so inconspicuous …bothered him so much. He was American but could never talk about that.

———

Exactly when he'd report in was just as anticipated as the stacks of papers in his in-basket. His secretary, Marti, was always good at putting Thelma's letters on top. He'd shuffle through the rest quickly pulling out what his eye might catch as timely or critical then sit down.

Thelma's letters were always first opened. Thelma had delivered Danielle in February 1948, and there was always news about baby and who came to visit. Even though he never asked Thelma for any, he longed to see photographs of the two of them. But it took almost three months for that first black and white snapshot to arrive.

After that when writing back, he'd spend most of his words about how cute the baby was and how well pretty Thelma's smile was captured on film. Marti gave him a shoebox to store these keepsakes, and Wally examined this trove of treasures every time as his first order of business.

Work issues were perpetually critical, and habitually important—so much so that daily reports also became routinely predictable. Wally dutifully thumbed through them, made comments in the margins, and red-penned or red-circled certain passages for follow-up. Marti devoted afternoons to taking notes from his recountings and then prepared internal documents for others' review. No matter how vital or how odd issues might be, there were always standard ways to handle them.

Before heading out on his next off-premise sojourn, Wally always met with the colonel in charge of the CIC. This is when innuendos, red flags, guesses, and touchy subjects were highlighted, and opinions shared. And, it's where Wally fared best because his data mining produced the most gold. The colonel usually did more listening than talking.

As he'd depart off-premise, he felt noticed and respected. He leaned forward when he walked. He felt like he mattered.

―――

Despite quiet desolation before Thelma could consider returning, Wally wasn't depressed. His meticulousness on the job gained more than a few trophy intel gems on a regular basis. His approach turned out to be fundamentally successful yet never particularly intimidating for anyone with whom he had a "business interest."

This is why his relationship with Berta was cultivated so carefully over this extended period of time. He first met her at the Konditorei, that same café serving those *mohrenkopfs* that he had enjoyed with Hilsa. But Berta was different. She had this status about her that gave her a look of inside authority whenever she entered or exited a room, whenever she expressed interest or asked questions. Did she even suspect his was American?

His initial interactions with P848 were cautious, even though camouflaged by his German-ness. She was charmed by Wally's take on things German in a new-Germany sense, and supportively exchanged bits of information that each thought might have some value. Politics was an easy subject for both. Touchy subjects were adroitly avoided.

She became the kind of friend he needed, a good coffee-shop colleague arguing strengths and weaknesses of people and events. The Communist Party, per se, wasn't particularly well-defined in the late 1940s; there were always what-if's, maybe-this's or maybe-that's, and neverending tête-à-têtes making for pleasant café sojourns for both. He became her friend too, perhaps for the same reasons.

Over time her intel tidbits became more tasty and tangible. He listened, interrupting only with good questions. She balanced this sparring with her own jousting. His journalistic aspirations became evident by these techniques as well. They both thrived complementing each other's style with mutual respect.

But again, her inconsistencies. He didn't judge her trepidation to talk about inside information, but he did detect how she chose to disclose details—inadvertent deductions that made her look erratic, maybe even a little capricious. But Wally deduced Berta was more absentminded than unreliable. It was also part of her parodies or whimsical personality.

Once she joked about things she disclosed to Wally with a droll smile, "…if you only knew what I'm telling you is private 'in-house' information …y'know, no one else can know this stuff."

"I won't publish one word about it either!"

Mutual trust had been gained.

Meanwhile, obscuring his state of mind in 1948 was that he wasn't sure when Thelma and Danielle needed to return to Germany. His daily work schedules were unpredictable of late, but he longed for family. Actual dates were postponed a few times until they settled on a date in the spring of 1949. The next thing Wally did was to move yet once again. He rented a secluded semi-furnished three bedroom apartment, a more urban place without a nosy landlord but with a private entrance to assure discreet comings and goings.

The day came with Thelma arriving aboard military aircraft. Wally was so happy to see her carrying baby Danielle off the plane. Though a cool spring day, he took them home in an open jeep; perhaps to appreciate the countryside, but so others could see him and his family together at least for a day. Family restored, he wouldn't have to read letters from Thelma anymore.

Berta, at 26, had completed secretarial school at the top of her class. She knew how to carry herself, how to dress smartly, and what it took to catch an eye …even down to ten carefully polished fingernails. Her good looks combined with expert administrative skills made her a particularly attractive recruit for the Party back in 1947.

Thus by early 1949, she and Wally were having routine political squabbles—fun tiffs producing further intel details he'd pen in his notebook later.

"Why aren't those with assets taking care of those with nothing?" She'd ask.

"Aren't they the ones who create jobs?"

"Jobs for themselves maybe. Let me tell you about this guy who…"

Even by the end of 1948, Berta didn't identify herself as an informer; she just had insights that piqued Wally's interest. Once he realized her position within the emerging Party, he invested more time, personality, and ultimately more persuasion into their relationship. He always picked up the tab for coffee and snacks; she thrived on his graciousness.

They had their own language, used puns and metaphors, made jokes about people and events they knew mutually; they could even synchronize their word choices to layer humor further. Others listening nearby simply couldn't grasp the wit.

Without ever having to say so, each eventually understood the other's allegiances. Respecting each other's vulnerabilities inside emergent German politics bonded the liaison.

As an educated, able administrator in the right place at the right time, she had become depended upon to retrieve and deliver information analyses during a time when the fledgling organization was re-forming itself. Being anti-Nazi, to be pro-communist at least in principal was relatively easy for her.

The Party's mission was being revised. Traces of old Nazism were being swapped inside an organization whose calling wasn't socialist in that kind of historical sense at all, but something more communist-oriented—an alternative to Nazism in the eyes of its leadership and a viable alternative to what citizens recently witnessed over the last two decades. Berta worked well for Homer Berger[4], an effective propagandist among the then forming leadership.

Within this small group of new-style reorganizers, by 1949 she kept getting more meaningful assignments until Homer agreed that she was *the* logical choice among staff to be promoted yet again. This time the big boss picked her to be one of his direct assistants. She was no longer a novice. *She was in the room!*

Meanwhile she and Wally enjoyed seconds (sometimes thirds) sipping *mohrenkopfs* once or twice a week. They both needed trusted empathy, commiserating about what was impacting West Germany at the time. To Berta, Wally was a *bon vivand* ... someone who liked to do the right things inside a reformatting society. Berta understood his progressive philosophy. Neither tried to persuade the other.

Whether they were being detected by insiders, surfaced

---

[4] Homer Berger was not his real name.

frequently in their chats; so they started experimenting having coffee elsewhere—places where no one at the next table might recognize either of them. But *were* they watching?

14

Max Reimann, incarcerated by German forces in 1939, had been cast into the infamous Hamm Prison (a notorious concentration camp) as enemy to existing Nazi interests in Czechoslovakia. By the end of World War II, Reimann became actively involved with socialist organizations, predecessors to the Communist Party.

He couldn't reconcile pursuing a second-tier position inside East Germany, but was successful seeking out and becoming Party chairman of West Germany by 1948.

Employed in various positions supporting this new communist-oriented Party in West Germany, Berta was exposed to a variety of planning probabilities and internal negotiations. Because of her education and applauded administrative skills, she rose into the ranks amid decision-makers and people with name recognition. Eventually, she had daily exposure with Max Reimann himself, not as a decision-maker but as a girl Friday who was counted on to create party communiques, discreetly deliver private messages ...an insider who understood who did what inside inner circles.

Communist interests gained ground throughout German countryside. Germany had been divided into four political sections at the end of the war for practical postwar supervision among the four (Great Britain, France, U.S., and U.S.S.R.) principal participants. Rapidly, territory congealed into two entities: east U.S.S.R.-controlled, and the other three. "East" and "West" connotations described this segmentation in the media.

Meanwhile, socialist idealism nurtured as a replacement for Nazism was growing too fast in the eyes the West. There were so few practices or customs to fall back upon that rules were penned and implemented too promptly and lacking complete assessment or consideration of alternatives. Both sides made mistakes, some work was sloppy.

Berta had opinions of her own about those *who* were making these rules—not necessarily with socialist ideologies she upheld. Though not completely realizing it, Berta was no longer just a chance informant, she was a full-fledged mole and she knew it. Guilt and complicity mingled with principles and purpose.

In a good position to encounter things others might not, Berta's chats now became analytically significant. She had begun to recognize Wally's ever-increasing inquisitiveness exchanging insights for over two years now, but by 1950 it passed a point of no return. What might happen if the wrong people learned they commiserated?

Ultimately she realized her own safety could be jeopardized if she continued to meet with her friend, just as easily as it could be jeopardized if she did not—an even tighter tightrope she knew she now walked.

———

Wally's military cohorts who needed to know she existed, knew her only as P848. The letter "P" was intelligence code for "prevention" to distinguish these informants from other useful local citizens. Hilsa and Berta had "P" designations.

The letter "O" was code for "ordinary" Germans, like

Werner, who assisted operations in a functional way, and "X" was code for support staff, like runners, who did not actually know anything but did things necessary for reconnaissance or transportation more naively. Every army staff person recognized these coded name-numbers, actual names were never used and remained never known.

———

Although no one at the cafés noticed it, in 1950 Wally was promoted to 1st lieutenant.

Meanwhile, Berta's tightrope quivered. Confiding having to maintain this awkward balance, his well-placed confidant became spirited about not wanting to be an informant anymore …or even to remain trapped in her present Party assignment. Discomfort began depreciating into greater insistence. "What can I do? I can't go on like this anymore…"

"You seem so …so troubled …something about to happen?"

"…it's the pressure." She began bargaining for ways to withdraw—many what-if questions followed by you-never-know conclusions. Even so, she reluctantly kept cooperating inside her delicate hope to keep this fragile two-camp status private. "I'm sure it'll pass. You've been kind to listen."

"Tell me more, Berta."

"Can't sleep. I just don't like where things are going." Her hands covered her eyes.

Information shared with Wally became more poignant, *more* laced with untoward intentions by the Party, *more* accented with events to come with names of those calling the shots …places and plans described *more* intrinsically. Within his counselor role, he exhibited no irritation or disapproval no matter how much or how little evidence was transferred on any one occasion.

But, everything was about to change.

Amid Berta's frustrations was one particular new fact she realized Wally would want to know; she deliberately decided not to disclose it. She knew her times with Wally would soon end.

———

Not immediately realized by Western intelligence as it was occurring, the Communist Party had been decentralizing several departments to other areas throughout Germany. It appeared to the U.S. Army that the Party itself was merely growing, and these movements were perceived no more than new offices. Quests for new intel elevated. Intercepted messages were deciphered. Moles were probed more aggressively.

Then at a routine coffee visit at their favorite café, that second *mohrenkopf* grew cold; P848 didn't show. Attempts to contact her later that day went void.

Days passed.

Nothing.

The *what* soon became clearer. What was actually happening was the next step of a preplanned piecemeal relocation of key headquarters operations from Frankfurt to Düsseldorf. It started back in 1948 without notice. By 1950, the *how* it could have been so successfully pulled off was not so clear.

Wally learned later Berta's time in Frankfurt had just ended, abruptly. She was probably taking the occasion to fade into her new city along with others who were missing in Frankfurt. But for Wally, that she just dropped off the map was like a punch in the stomach. That she didn't give him any advance warning or even an inkling, was a double whammy.

Had she been summoned to Berlin? Or, worse?

Now what?

———

Complicating communications, the newly formed German Federal Republic's (West German) government could not remain sitting in Berlin.

Berlin had become a city dominated by U.S.S.R.-oriented management. This is why West Germany's new Bundestag had to reestablish a working parliament in Bonn, a medium-sized city between Düsseldorf and Frankfurt. Many thought it a temporary necessity.

The Bundestag, established in 1949, was successor to the earlier Reichstag, governing body (i.e., parliament) for the German Federal Republic upon enactment of its new constitution. Since West Berlin wasn't officially under constitutional jurisdiction (it was in *East* Germany) coupled with the advent of awkward postwar relationships, the Bundestag simply had to meet in Bonn instead of Berlin.

Furthermore, owing to Berlin's legal status, West Berliners were unable to vote in Bundestag elections, and were represented by twenty non-voting delegates, indirectly elected by the city's House of Representatives.

It didn't take long for everyone to understand that Bonn's functional relocation was permanent. It had become the capital of West Germany in fact.

Government operations were in disorderly states as were political parties, protesters, businesses, and citizens relocating for a second or third time—including, of course, the Communist Party itself.

———

Up to this time, Wally's precious mole had been providing extraordinary pieces of far-reaching intelligence that kept notebook pages worn out from repetitive reviews.

Unexpectedly, key phone numbers now no longer worked.

Other informants evaporated from their usual rendezvous as well. No one knew what became of their productive informants and several other real party members who suddenly no longer lived in Frankfurt. The once prolific data well had dried up.

Carriage returns on typewriters ceased to bang. Coffee cups were empty.

What happened to P848?

15

Wally's field work went flat for weeks at a time. Walking streets turned into writing reports, rereading old ones, revising others', filing paper, commiserating in bathrooms about all those what-if questions. The CIC Colonel was grumpy.

"Ah ...*mohrenkopfs*, where are they when you need them" he mumbled to himself out loud staring at yet another empty coffee pot.

One day in his in-basket a new assignment claimed his attention. It dealt with negotiations regarding U.S. military maneuvering rights—permissions the U.S. had to seek officially in order to reposition troops inside West Germany, required now that it had regained full authority as an independent country. He traveled to Heidelberg regularly, useful interruptions to paper-shuffling.

But on-the-street information gathering seemed a dead end alley.

Before sitting down, he stood looking at his desk with

vertical wrinkles between his eyes. Lips pursed, his hands casually grasped his waist in an "I'm-not-sure" pose. Even though he kept his ears open and probed tidbits of intel that piqued his craving for snooping around, it seemed most days were re-reading old notes to gain something previously missed. Hilsa showed up less often, and offered little new. Even she couldn't figure out what had happened to many she knew.

Sipping *mohrenkopfs* at Konditorei wasn't the same. The only one drinking a *mohrenkopf*, Wally looked out the windows. The crowds were different. He scrutinized other coffee drinkers bearing too many smiles, too much joking around. He wasn't included. He walked the sidewalks. Alone. This wouldn't do.

Wally began looking under rugs again.

Once the Party's headquarters move to Düsseldorf was suspected then verified, efforts were employed to locate where people had been reassigned. Wally was of course drawn to what happened to P848 specifically.

Among productive Frankfurt "P" numbers who had apparently departed, none connected with any of the "P-type" informants already in Düsseldorf.

Other local moles lived in empty nests—reporting nothing except what was already known.

Stealth captured contemplations. With a few tips, and a couple well-placed inquiries, he studied how skeptical innuendos from one source evolved into speculations about another. He eventually determined Berta had *probably* relocated to Düsseldorf or Berlin. Tracking her down didn't bear fruit since she changed addresses, phone numbers, and all means of contact. There weren't even any other less critically positioned moles who could verify her new assignment let alone her existence. Wally took some chances.

Week after week, he meticulously made dumb calls about mundane issues to people not likely to suspect his motive. He might characterize himself as a party member using typical communist parlance. Sometimes he'd play a supplier or tradesman using regional slang or jargon to dispel suspicion but gain tidbits of information. When suitable, he'd drop her name here and there then keep asking otherwise senseless questions gaining pieces of seemingly meaningless information that he assembled into jigsaw-puzzle-type scenarios.

There were abundant possibilities, lots of "maybe" pieces to assemble. Week after week passed, but he didn't give up.

Then one time, "I've been trying to deliver a box to this tall blonde lady, maybe you know her, Bette, Anna …something like that."

"Oh, you must mean Berta?" a junior assistant surmised questioningly.

His heart skipped a beat. Seizing the moment, he gained a phone number for that blonde lady in Düsseldorf. Surely it must be her …surely …or, was it just another maybe? Wally cued the colonel who said "don't hold your breath, lieutenant."

Before touching that black phone, he stared at the surreptitiously garnered number, memorizing it while recapturing that well-dressed business-woman image embedded in his mind. Did he need to rehearse what to say? Should he merely say "hello"? Would she hang up on him? Imagination preempting duty finally came to an end. He picked up the receiver, paused again picturing perfectly manicured fingernails twelve inches away from another black telephone on a desk just beyond a stack of papers …somewhere tucked away in a shade-drawn poorly lit office in Düsseldorf.

He dialed visualizing her hands grasping the phone with a prompt, perhaps surprised jerk. He closed his eyelids. Eleven weeks had now passed since he had last heard her voice. He knew she'd link her jerk with a don't-bother-me-right-now frown before pasting on the office smile usually accompanying her business voice. After three rings, he wondered if the number was genuine then reasoned no one was actually there after the fifth. At seven spirits sagged, one eyebrow lifted. Was all this for naught? At nine, he pressed his chin grimacing.

On the tenth, Berta's inimitable voice answered with a curt but recognizable, well-contrived routine business, "yes? …hello, whom do you wish to speak to?"

"Hi there," Wally enunciated his language in a low, slow, polite but familiar voice, "this is your old friend! I still have your dry cleaning. Can you pick it up?"

Recognizing his voice instantly, she paused for a whole

second before acknowledging the dry cleaning. They talked for less than ten seconds, full-well knowing there could likely be phone taps. She agreed to pick it up near that café in Düsseldorf after lunch tomorrow by 1:30—an otherwise potentially dangerous thing to do.

Wally was desperate not to lose her into that ever-churning communist bureaucracy—so much had been gained—so much yet to go. His heart pumped blood almost audibly. Would she show?

Parked near the busy café, he waited becoming privately agitated. At 2:15, she finally walked around the corner with forced nonchalance, browsing in storefront windows close to the café, occasionally looking over her shoulders …a private way to see and be seen. Once she noticed him, she dropped her chin inconspicuously signaling acknowledgement, looked both ways, and crossed the street.

Meanwhile, Wally started his car and inched it unhurriedly into shadows of a nearby building. P848 discreetly got into his car, gently clicking the door closed.

"It's good to see you again," Wally said in a friendly tone, leaning to his right and then giving her a kiss on her cheek. "I missed you, Berta." Those eleven weeks now no longer mattered. He shifted gears driving away slowly, and back onto the crowded boulevard.

Berta looked straight ahead. Dressed well in dark blue wrinkle-free business attire with a white tailored blouse, she carried herself seriously. Thumb and forefinger massaging her chin, she then her hand fall. She tried to look relaxed but couldn't pull it off. He noticed her flawlessly smooth hands restraining nervousness as she clutched a small dark blue leather purse. "I know," is all she could utter in an apologetic whisper.

Heading for a nearby safe house, Wally anticipated she'd update him on all pending issues. Both courteous and more business-like than previous visits, they entered the room and sat at the table. Wally poured water from a readied pitcher on the table into two waiting glasses.

Though time was precious, he didn't force speech on irrelevant topics but got to familiarities in usual style. A willingness to connect again was evident, but her face conveyed apprehension.

She said softly, "you may not believe me, but it's really good to see you again too. But things have changed." Berta explained rationales behind the Düsseldorf move, her elevated responsibilities, and new hazards she contended with.

On one hand, to reestablish shared confidences, Wally put all he could into convincing Berta of her essential value and how much he appreciated her work. On the other, she tried to persuade him she no longer wanted to play this role. Avoiding looking at him directly, she scrutinized her thumbs rubbing fingers instead …afraid.

Upon regaining her eyes for an instant, he said "I want you to know, although I'm a journalist, not one thing we've talked about has gone to the press. I respect our professional friendship, and I'm not interested in publicizing anything."

She looked down. In closed quarters, perceived risk levels had elevated so much, she pressed her left ring finger with the thumb and index finger from her right hand—then switched the one hand to massage the other. Instead of looking at Wally, she examined her perfectly groomed nails as she disclosed yet another intel detail. She repeated this laborious process over and over while he patiently said nothing more …only nodding an understanding tilt of his head to express approval for her bumpy recital.

Though Berta's stress levels had risen, familiar names and a few forthcoming events gradually manifested. He urged her to continue using his hands.

Berta indicated she wasn't sure how much longer she could survive as an informant. Mutual respect was regenerated because he knew how to talk in his practiced nonthreatening way. They both knew he had the aces in this tension-stuck poker game. Still, they had become good friends. Neither would intentionally cause harm to the other; each knew what the other needed. No words were necessary.

He learned it was her intention to fade into the bureaucracy with less conspicuous assignments and a lower profile than she had in Frankfurt. It would surely generate less stressful working environments for her. But it couldn't be sustained; she had no bargaining chips.

Her two roles had to continue: Communist assistant, and

informant. So she acquiesced. Her act of submission was hard to define. Compliance seemed to convey more surrender than agreement, more resignation than intent. He put his hand over her writhing knuckles. They said nothing more for two or three minutes—nothing more until she nodded being ready to depart.

In that less than twenty-five minute rendezvous, substantial information was still yielded. They agreed to meet again in a week. An already-wrapped package of dry cleaning was waiting in Wally's car which she knew she'd need to take with her. No further words were spoken. She exited the car in the same alley and walked away without glancing back. he let the car idle until she was out of sight.

———

Düsseldorf became their new hometown. For two more years, they met regularly just never in exactly the same place. She carefully expanded intel transfers—transfers that unquestionably went on to become fatefully consequential. But three-fourths of their commiseration was about world affairs, commerce, and new developments in the West, like televisions and fast cars. But each time Wally spent the last ten minutes educating Berta how to be more security conscious, how not to leave paper trails, when to select routes not always seen publicly, and why to choose different ways to get to same place the second time. Habitually deviating routines made her less predictable. Always having logical (easily substantiated) reasons to be away was the number one new practice.

Wally knew she valued these interactions. This accepted advice was like acquiring body armor she'd need to use every day.

P848 was becoming a meticulous to-the-core informant displaying predictably unpredictable behaviors like a pro. Her mannerisms in speech were like her hands and fingers: nimble, flawlessly manicured, clean, and coupled with an attorney-like voice abundant with fertile information handed off regularly ... and judiciously.

It turned out she had become one of the primary conduits

between the Communist Party in West Germany to the one in East Germany. Carrying an attaché when leaving Düsseldorf, she made trips to Berlin as Max Reimann's personal envoy—an attaché stuffed with papers intended for others' eyes. Upon her return this black leather attaché was empty. The East German Party had its own conduits carrying even fatter attachés west, and often it was more than just one attaché for Max's consumption.

"You should see what comes from *Moscow* to Berlin!" she chortled raising an eyebrow. "Less paper than you'd imagine. Yet, I've seen wincing when they open envelopes …sometimes their reactions tell me more than words on paper."

Information flow was abundant east to west. P848's contributions were therefore speculative, peppered with "if" statements even though these iffy observations played out repeatedly as she'd conjecture.

Because of layered complexities getting info to the top, the administrative nature of P848's role permitted her privy to secret conversations traveling from East to West as well. In fact, a few times she reported information to Wally before Max himself heard it.

Tensions mounted. Backroom angsts elevated with deteriorating newspaper reports. Berta cancelled meetings, apologizing when events blocked regular chats. Face-to-face tête-à-têtes were quicker, shorter. Using coded jargon—phrases or expressions communicating complicated thoughts needing no further discussion, even a one minute exchange on the street contained valuable data using such connived idioms. No time for coffee.

Should any of Berta's wayward behaviors or ruses been uncovered by anyone inside the Party, she would likely have made a one-way eastbound trek to Berlin then never be seen or heard from again.

When together in safe houses, P848 either read from her notebook or gave Wally notes she'd written. When handing paper to him, Wally could tell she worried about what might happen if these penned summaries were mislaid or somehow got back to others she knew. Every time he touched these papers, he assured these were precious and in safe hands. Then he'd give her a gentle lecture about being careful with paper notes and notebooks.

Meetings were time conscious, business-oriented, and short. Even so, there were moments of humor or resignation to things, or comments about personalities—like when she'd remark about how bizarrely Max grimaced when getting directive suggestions (i.e., orders) from Berlin. Max's facial expressions implied conflicting conclusions for P848 to observe which she shared with Wally amid mutual chuckles. Max had two faces, one public for Berlin bosses and local staff, and one private that he exhibited only with those capturing his immediate reactions. Wally found Berta's observations useful for grasping subtleties inside Max's intentions.

Lt. Rothwell became educated about origins of subversive activities penned by the East German Communist Party in Berlin that probably were authored in Moscow. Until then, public protests in West Germany couldn't be attributed to the Party in the East. Many protests dealt with specific anti-NATO or anti-U.S. activities—like organizing political demonstrations among students, stirring up community discontent, shaping a more conventional Communist Party, or other actions against a recovering West-oriented German government still in its infancy.

Some activities were not blocked even though they could have been. These were monitored to substantiate (and document) the accuracy of P848's detailed data. Wally's commander was careful with facts thus transferred assuring identities would never be compromised. Something significant was about to occur.

———

In late fall 1951, unanticipated detours sidetracked routine maneuverings as Wally encountered tussles with the 970th Command itself. For undisclosed reasons, data from P848 turned out to be so consequential that missing parts became even higher priorities to acquire. Pressure built on Lt. Rothwell to extract certain key intel from her …more often. Even though Berta usually demurred with class when so confronted, soon P848 didn't comply as quickly or as often for reasons she didn't disclose. This mystery was chilling.

Wally had to get up earlier, spend more time feeding the intel pipeline via other sources, find new sources, get to bed later. Even Hilsa began asking Wally about things her usual sources couldn't provide. Tension among most of the Ps and Os was noticeable.

Thelma had become pregnant a second time.

The *Red Menace* was advancing. When such words were uttered, a minced side-glance became part of this contrived verbal autograph for Communist threats. While such words had been used colloquially behind closed doors, they now emerged into print as well; and, by late 1951 they had entered everybody's vocabulary.

Berta and Wally's more or less smooth-again arrangement hit a deep pothole that winter.

16

Lieutenant Rothwell's five year stint in Germany was due to end in six months. Though he made requests to extend his assignment, it was denied upstairs by the general in charge of army operations. Though such denials were normal procedure, he and his CIC colonel were both disappointed; so much had been invested, so much vital information had been gained. In November 1951, an able successor, Hans, had been screened carefully and selected to replace Wally upon his anticipated rotation late spring, 1952.

Coaching the new guy on subtleties inside the Berta-Wally relationship began by Christmas so transitions could be achieved without interruption. Week after week of half-day sessions, Lt. Rothwell groomed him on intricacies and nuances that made this special arrangement work. The protégé made good marks with intelligence collecting, could speak fluent local German, and looked the part. By late January, Wally readied for that inevitable meeting when he'd disclose to P848 what was going to happen to his "old friend."

The day came, the twosome had coffee. Berta became visibly wary learning the news—eyebrows twitching, she avoided eye contact. Though never saying no, the bond with this "old friend" was complicated and laden upon years of cautiously built trust. Looking down, she shook her head in a restrained pressed-lip "oh, no" side-to-side forced acquiescence that he couldn't soothe.

As she began withdrawing emotionally, in the back of his head he wondered whether she would once again disappear. He just couldn't let that happen. Patiently, he said little more, waiting for the worst to abate. Finally, she took a very deep breath, looked up with a forced business-trained smile. Intense quiet lingered as they pondered the moment. Wally whispered a request for a next meeting; the two agreed to meet again in a week as a threesome.

He and his successor prepared diligently for this next session. When both finally met together at a private out of the way café, unexpectedly her reaction exhibited passionate resignation. She sarcastically characterized herself as a commodity being bartered away. In low accusing tones, "...and you, Hans! How would *you* know what's *really* happening?" she growled at the young soldier. "...do you care? ... what can you give me? ...are we mere conduits of information?" The novice was caught dumbfounded by her intensity, apparently unable to create any immediate mutual confidence despite his resonant deep voice, gentle spirit, and a few calming words. They politely let her vent.

Wally sensed withdrawal insinuations as her mannerisms cooled, "we've talked about this day coming a few times. How should we manage this, Berta? Help me out here."

She nervously massaged her left fingers with her right thumb and index finger again. Then with arms crossing her chest, effective information transfers hit a roadblock. Hands shaking when she did talk, she uttered meaningless words, repeated political clichés or dogmatic mantras, all interspersed with otherwise forced-polite remarks reflecting personal isolation. No information was gained even though a form of calm acceptance was achieved. Berta agreed to meet again.

Despite the CIC colonel's insistence otherwise later that morning, a next threesome meeting had been scheduled for

Tuesday week. Why the colonel was so perplexed about the delay was never explained.

———

Things deteriorated further.

On Tuesday, the threesome met at a coffee shop near the university. This time it looked as if she were ready to face the ultimate consequences. Berta's hair wasn't combed smartly, no makeup, her eyes reflected dark circles—with sadness weighing down her brows. She kept clearing her throat. Wally thought about that one-way ticket to Berlin. Since it could no longer continue as it had, he wondered whether she felt anger, disappointment, or surrender—yet she didn't say no to yet further meetings— threesomes producing little meaningful data for the CIC.

Over subsequent weeks, it wasn't as if ongoing snippets of intel went completely missing; it was that they were slowly drying up while pressures on P848's two interrogators intensified. Wally knew just enough about what his commander wanted documented, to know he was falling short. Exactly what was so urgent or meaningful, however, remained ambiguous. When colonel declared something "desperately needed," it was attributed to *someone* upstairs without detail.

Because of the impending departure, Marti made sure Wally's admin roles were transferred to her new boss over the next three months. As Hans worked hard gaining needed street skills, Wally's job grew smaller. Looking through winter-spring rains, Lt. Rothwell spent more time at the windows becoming more and more frustrated. He couldn't grasp the political urgencies or colonel's change in behavior.

Once a week meetings with P848 continued producing sparse harvests. Hans wasn't as effective turning the P848 medium into never-ending data as expected. The more the rookie applied his better-developed and friendly interrogation style Wally had taught him, the more there were periods where Berta stressed out, broke down, or became unstable. It wasn't easy to explain why, but all three recognized roadblocks for what they were. A next meeting was always agreed to each time.

———

It was February 1952, and Thelma was now due to deliver their second child.

———

Originating after the war and escalating over the next five or six years, ultimate Communist goals were, cause by cause, country by country, gradually revealed to the West. At first it was tolerated as postwar consequences to be managed over time. But for the West, a better political response to USSR's surging interest in spreading Party principles was needed. It was finally accepted as a confrontational hurdle central Europe had to face.

The Soviet Union had begun a process of annexing countries as new republics joining USSR itself, exploiting the merits of secret agreements with Nazi Germany that the West didn't fully appreciate at first. Parts of Poland and Finland were incorporated into USSR. Others (Lithuania, Estonia, and Latvia) were devalued into lesser republics literally sewn into the Soviet structure. Yet others (like Czechoslovakia and Poland) became satellite states tied and beholden to the Communist Party.

Internally, opposing political parties were unashamedly oppressed allowing the now stronger Communist Party to capture "elected" governing posts and impose their influence further at the local level. In Poland, when massive Communist-oriented land reforms and nationalizations were voted upon by its population and then vigorously defeated, it took a second vote-rigged election to redefine and achieve the preferred Communist-desired results.

Borders throughout Eastern Europe fluctuated. Coupled with fluid population movements trying to reestablish indigenous homelands, maps continued to change. Acts of intrusion penetrated local cultures with unusual efficiency inside beleaguered communities—local villages that hadn't yet recovered from devastating damages to infrastructure, property, and huge losses of life just a few years prior.

Were winds blowing in from East Germany polluting the weather in West Germany? Some *New Germans* reckoned so. By winter 1951-52, prevailing media contended a more formal political response to stop Soviet advances must be advanced. For the West, especially the U.S., it became international bluff-calling times.

———

Thelma and Wally had their second child, Linda. Born in Germany at the U.S. Army Hospital in Frankfurt, she became an American citizen immediately. Lt. Rothwell had been on-duty officer at the hospital the night she was born (getting another on-duty officer to take his place was tricky that night, but serendipity prevailed).

Looking ahead a few months, the four Rothwells would be readying for their east to west journey across the Atlantic at the end of this five year tour of duty. Thelma anticipated all the positives getting her own family closer to things North American.

By April, Hans tried talking to P848 on his own. The only thing he knew was instead of golden information she had been delivering to Wally in years past along with a few little nuggets inside the threesome's chats, she was now barely providing occasional flakes of information—perhaps only enough to survive.

Hans couldn't defend either to Wally or an ever-wincing colonel why she was missing meetings. Each time, that one-way eastbound ticket was reassessed as becoming likely. So, the colonel recommended a further series of threesome meetings to gain specific information about Max on one hand, and to placate Berta on the other. Her demeanor did improve, but data flows were encumbered with strange scraps of inexplicable innuendoes that she had heard—overheard about things even she couldn't identify. Meanwhile, CIC staff privately exhibited concern over her survival.

In the meantime, as the generals displayed tightlipped acquiescence about discussions behind closed doors, everyone knew Communist social movements were infiltrating West

Germany. Though these upstairs conclaves among the "star-lapelled management" started in 1951, lately the CIC's colonel groused about them under his breath. Everyone wondered who attended these "upstairs" meetings. Were data sources being disclosed? Need they prepare for something?

On-the-street intelligence gathering lost its casual clothing as it blended into alley shadows. No one on the street wanted to be seen *by* anyone *with* anyone. Trusts were challenged …violence was implied then openly threatened …Party-induced rallies became too noisy and disruptive to ignore. A few regulars disappeared that spring. Even Hilsa's eavesdropping revealed imminence of something "else" inside the clamor and chatter of the conflicting objectives she overheard.

Intel droughts from usual sources were turning into other forms of useless prophecy. Stacks of unsubstantiated ambiguity and overflowing trash bins from yesterday's guesses overshadowed those more productive (now empty) in-baskets. Even the 970th commander couldn't explain surges of trivial nuances from his own staff. Were these merely filling voids?

Sidebar source references to "P848" had been central on briefing notes for years; now even this motherlode was drying up. Wally's personal frustration developed into exasperation, an anxiety he felt that he too was being thrown away like a commodity. Nobody talked about what or who really mattered. No news bred wild speculations.

On the surface, it appeared nothing new was coming from P848. Hans searched for ways to make it productive, pumping Wally for insights. Even little crumbs about placenames or particular people were gobbled up the next morning when they wrote up their findings and hypotheses. As Wally penned his own words, he couldn't help consider how Berta had to endure conjectures from her Party cohorts. They met as a threesome only once more.

———

Totally unbeknownst to our two interrogators, high-ranking

members of the 970th Command had begun collaborating with their counterparts along with members of the West German Supreme Court *sub rosa* during the winter and spring of 1951-52. In private chambers, testimonies were scrutinized so U.S. undercover assumptions about future operations in West Germany could be explained. Much of the pertinent evidence had been gained directly via P848 over the last 18-24 months. Adding her four year history of accurate assessments was prodigious and persuasive.

But the Supreme Court only knew the source as "P848." From Wally's point of view, once P848's identity was compromised, some form of protection would be absolutely required on her behalf. If the 970th abandoned her, that noose around her neck would tighten with finality. It had become a teetering house of cards. Since the colonel was unforthcoming about what information was being shared, a diagnosis of what was to be gained politically big picture couldn't be determined. Wally could only grasp who was likely to be lost. Was he now handing over that noose so this remarkable woman would never be seen again?

It was now only a handful of weeks before Lt. Rothwell was scheduled to cross the Atlantic. He explained his mindset to the colonel who listened but said little except to confirm confidentiality of P848's real name. This had to be accepted for what it was.

————

As spring bloomed along the Rhine, pressures continued to elevate inside private offices of the 970th. By May just days before he and his family's departure, he learned that full disclosures including informants' names were being shared openly with the West German Supreme Court. Though P848's real name had indeed now been revealed, there was no word on where Berta physically might be.

Future Party intentions, leadership objectives, and subversive internal activities that P848 had carefully disclosed, turned out to be more consequential than anyone might ever have fathomed at the time. Her predictions had come true as anticipated, lending high credibility to other key Party purposes, now imminent.

The Court had been impressed by the depth of multifaceted minutiae the 970th had accumulated; specifics were profoundly persuasive. It predicted demonstrations, named names, and pinpointed tactics local groups were choosing to use. Beyond this, precisely listed connections to the East German Communist Party with consequent associations to Moscow were enumerated and well documented.

Since Lt. Rothwell didn't have to testify personally, he couldn't know exactly what was going on so he presumed much less than realities behind doors. But a lot was indeed happening *sub rosa.*

Throughout the 970th, levels of secrecy were unyielding, strictly observed even in bathrooms and cafeterias. Perspiration, nervous hands, and rounded eyes were common.

Rothwell's military tour wrapped up. Everybody knew he was heading "home" soon—to his country of birth, to all the good places and all the good people all the "everybody else's" longed to see. For others heading home, it was smiles for them and envious looks from those who stayed behind. Straight-faced Wally shook hands but remained sober.

As the Rothwells were packing suitcases, Wally kept seeking clues. Though something big must be breaking upstairs, no one offered anything except heartfelt goodbyes and hugs. On their journey home, others aboard the plane were anticipating family, reunions, and apple pie. But exactly how P848 might likely have been compromised or restrained or imprisoned festered in his meditations as the plane bounced from one cloud to the next.

A rush of duties upon arrival in the U.S. was overwhelming: new uniforms, a new residence for the Rothwell Four, transportation. Everyone spoke English. He checked in at the Maryland post, the only place in America where he already knew his way around.

––––––––––

As a result of multi-layered substantiation from P848 including evidence gained from a few other well-placed informants, the West German Supreme Court continued evaluating whether to declare the Communist Party as subversive, harmful to the emerging culture, and therefore no longer legal in the country. Few people knew this was underway.

After considering alternatives, a mutually acceptable resolution was finally achieved in large part recognizing P848's so consequential contributions. Only by mid-1952, mere weeks after Wally had physically departed Germany, did the world learn the results. Even he heard the news on one of those newfangled television contraptions.

For two days, he didn't know any specifics about whether anything had been agreed upon with respect to Berta. It had been crucial to protect P848, but now her survival was in jeopardy. Had she been just a bargaining chip? Not knowing was excruciatingly perplexing. After unsuccessful attempts to uncover details unfolding a few thousand miles away, he finally did receive direct word from his former CIC commander. It was affirmation only for what was essential to know, nothing more. It was personal courtesy, an act of mutual respect that his colonel extended. For security and safety reasons, Wally learned only two things.

- First, P848 was indeed included in the highly selective and limited group for resettlement in the United States. The program was similar to legal witness-protection plans. She received an entirely new identity.

- Second, he learned that she had successfully made it to U.S. soil.

After his commander's one-minute phone call, he graciously thanked him and felt relieved. He never even once saw her or heard from her or about her ever again; but at least she was safe. It was still a particularly remarkable event since very few informants ever received this level of treatment, indeed a political "pass" that had to be approved by the head of the CIA himself. But it was also a gold star on Lt. Rothwell's military employment record.

Again he donned his uniform with silver bars as he readjusted to an almost foreign but indeed American venue. Again he lived in the United States—it seemed for the first time. For five years, 1947-52, he had lived the life of an undercover spy—a consequential covert agent.

————

His secretary, Marti, retired from army duties once Wally transferred home. She continued living in Europe instead of returning to the U.S. and eventually chose to live on the French Riviera.

He smiled when he learned later on that Hans had struck a working relationship with Hilsa. She would thrive dispensing to Hans her social views about ideal societies, and how the now-secret Party's efforts had become so much more surreptitious. But Hilsa was no Berta.

————

Amid all the concealment and backstage hullabaloos leading up to that striking move in1952, the West German Supreme Court finally and publicly declared their decision to ban the Communist Party for a minimum of fourteen years.

Though it took a few years to fully implement, this upheaval—indeed international slap in the face—could not be tolerated by the Soviets. But it had to be since they were not positioned well for any sort of formal declaration of war. Besides, reconstruction was still occurring throughout Europe including Russia. An icy compromise surfaced since no one could again afford real war.

The King of England had died in February. Queen Elizabeth began setting a new stage—a new rallying point for the British to gather around. For Europe as well, everyone seemed not only to want a new page to turn, but wanted an entirely new chapter to begin.

Considering World War II ending only seven years prior and how underdeveloped the West German political infrastructure was, the decision to outlaw the Party was a significant historical decision—a decision that undulated back against a frigidly cool reception throughout Eastern Europe. Though summer, political frost now lay on the ground everywhere.

Slowly it became a series of tit for tat political skirmishes, on-the-ground obstructions, and blatant noncooperation, shots across the proverbial bow—everything anyone could think of short of actual confrontational armed conflict.

It was a new kind of warfare.

This clash of opposing spirits bore signatures affirmed in newspapers and magazines. The "red menace" wouldn't disappear—instead it became a sticky concept glued to news commentaries and political conversations everywhere—a concept that gained traction on both sides of that hardening north-to-south Iron Curtain. By 1952, it was inserted into to everyone's ideological vocabulary on the street as well.

Rationalizing this drama throughout the world, two new words described it succinctly: Cold War.

17

Once Wally's five year tour of duty in postwar Germany ended, he turned from a covert German-oriented back-alley spy wearing a fine long leather jacket into a conspicuous professor of advanced espionage strategies in full army uniform. He was the go-to guy for tactical how-to advice for intel solutions and future undercover discoveries no matter where he went.

But upon returning to Fort Holabird, army intelligence capital in the U.S., life changed on many different fronts aside from his new more starched-khaki-oriented profession.

First, Thelma and their two children found a new home in America. Canadian-raised Thelma and Swiss-raised Wally were indeed becoming an international family—neither daughter was born in the U.S. as well (i.e., Canada and Germany).

For 29-year-old Walter H. Rothwell, Jr., it was the first opportunity to learn what it was like to live in his native-born country, as father and husband, and as a citizen.

Thelma and Wally inhabited what might have been a 1950s

white-picket-fence lifestyle with a four door Buick, a three foot thick television, grocery shopping at the PX or Safeway—frozen TV dinners and potato chips on their TV trays. They even had a pet dog.

Baltimore, a large city, offered much to satisfy city dwellers whether it be bistros or boutiques, symphonies or sports. American culture was absorbed thoroughly.

But, everybody spoke English.

By March 1954, now *Captain* Rothwell was ready to turn another diary page. Though prominent in his field, sometimes duties were too tedious and predictable—those exciting times and risky situations were gone ...lingering only in memory. Telling the story about Berta simply could not happen ...that remained secret. And, *doing* the work was better than reciting how-to techniques; he couldn't support professorial techniques with provable feats.

So, he sought other hands-on opportunities.

———

In 1955, as "Intelligence Battalion" leader, he was assigned the task moving 200-300 troops (about 75% enlisted plus one female nurse) in uniform from Fort Mead, Maryland, to Fort Hood, Texas. The planned-in-advance four week scripted exercises were special maneuvers verifying battalion mobility on one hand, and practicing staged "undercover" operations performing interrogation and other investigative techniques with Fort Hood soldiers once they got there, on the other. On top of that, it took an additional week just getting to Texas, and another week to make it back home again.

This was a big project!

The caravan of jeeps and trucks and troops traipsed over the Appalachians on narrow roads, across the South avoiding bigger cities to get to Fort Hood with the least local disruption. But keeping this caterpillar-like entourage of vehicles more or less sidewinding together was just one of many challenges.

Finding places to spend the night was one difficulty. Motels were rented along the way, and multiple soldiers occupied each room; but, coordinating several motels miles apart for any one night's stay was awkward to synchronize.

Another unanticipated dilemma occurred when Captain Rothwell faced objections from local desk clerks or owners who wouldn't permit black soldiers to sleep in their rooms. Excessive racial biases remained widespread, especially in rural communities in 1950s Deep South.

Whenever the battalion faced such objections, he'd raise hell with the managers, and vehemently insist all troops be accommodated. Not even one soldier would be denied a room. While there were sometimes dramatic verbal protests to his insistence black soldiers be so lodged, he prevailed every time.

At meal times, similar objections occurred when soldiers stopped for food. And again, Captain Rothwell succeeded assuring all men ate whatever they wanted to eat, ate together in the same diningroom facility, and at the same tables.

New bedrooms and each meal were renegotiated every single day.

Fort Hood was an immense army base. But even considering its mammoth size, several obstacles billeting a couple hundred extra soldiers existed. Actual housing ended up at a separate army base near the fort. They commuted each day each way.

Substantial tactical exercises at Fort Hood had been painstakingly preplanned. Exercises were designed to demonstrate how to capture and interrogate prisoners during war, but it also included how to respond *if* captured. Rehearsal drills were conducted in outdoor and indoor venues with a variety of scenarios depicting likely conditions.

Some troops played the role of POWs (prisoners of war), some as guards, others as foreign or American interrogators. Each afternoon, each group's performances were evaluated, perhaps repeated the next day or supported by further training. Assessments evaluated how well friendly groups interacted with each other as if real war were going on.

Environments changed frequently and unpredictably— controlled chaos. Each day embodied vigorous physical training for the battalion as well as local soldiers, often extending well into the night.

Though just a "game," exercises had been deliberately designed to be mentally stressful and physically grueling. Soldiers took their roles seriously. Interrogation techniques focused on what worked and what didn't to gain the right kind of information fulfilling the mission. Dramatic, real life performances were reenacted over and over the whole month to train soldiers in these techniques.

Further, Wally's own battalion practiced how to log such events in the field then apply protocols on how to write documentation for use by others later. There were always boxes of ball point pens lying around.

When they weren't in the field, they were in the classroom often wearing dust-laden uniforms from that morning's quasi-hostile activities.

One Saturday night at Fort Hood to lighten the mood and break up routines, Wally entertained a large group of soldiers at the Officers' Club playing jazz piano. His nimble fingers raced up and down those black keys in rhythms that captured the finger and toe tapping audience for over two hours. No one knew about his musical abilities.

Washing uniforms was postponed to Sunday night.

The trip home to Maryland was another week spent navigating new routes over the Appalachians with now-familiar restaurant and motel negotiating skills under their belts.

———

The following year, Wally took an area study course about the Dominican Republic. The purpose was to research economic and cultural landscapes within the country. He then wrote an extensive essay in support of army priorities.

There was always another course to take, another paper to write, another task to handle.

Sometimes it was translating memos or deciphering implications of German, French, even Italian messages, or describing subtleties of the writer's phraseology. He'd often say:

"Here's what the guy said, but this is what he really meant by saying it this way."

There were other assignments as well. For example, he was often the one selected to be the U.S. Army escort for foreign dignitaries visiting America: one time it was the Commanding General of the Belgian army, another the French Director of Army Personnel, yet another the West German Officer of Intelligence. He was the primary go-to army officer whenever such services were needed.

Wally earned certificates, diplomas, badges, and letters of commendation augmenting his already multi-page résumé. His five year stint at Fort Mead was laced with a variety of missions.

But as this five year stint was rounding up, Captain Rothwell realized he was intrinsically more valuable to the US Army in Europe than in the United States.

The Rothwell family flew east across the Atlantic. After having been Americanized for five years, there was still positive anticipation—a different kind of anticipation. In a way, they were going home to Germany.

Wally's credentials preceded him. The Cold War in 1957, after all, continued to linger. Soldiers, like Lt. Rothwell, who translated innuendo and drew useful conclusions from the mumbo jumbo that typically clogged understanding and reaction time, were always on stage, ready—but behind the curtains—inconspicuous. His business cards were forever stashed away for safekeeping.

18

After having earned prestige that comes with experience, Wally was thereafter groomed with both name recognition and reputation. From 1957 to 1962, he bounced from one classroom to the next, sometimes an instructor, sometimes a consultant. Chalk boards and erasers were his tools.

Thelma and their two daughters were pretty excited about living in Frankfurt again. Danielle and Linda, in particular, were both gaining international experiences others their age weren't likely to have. Evidence of war was not forgotten, but no longer visible. Captain Rothwell was usually home on time for dinner. He and Thelma even had time for an occasional espresso under brightly colored umbrellas.

But this tour of duty was different from the last time.

Seldom did he have the opportunity for *mohrenkopfs*, but

when he did, he found himself chatting with other, older coffee drinkers who were looking for ears to bend—and he let himself slide into conversations as if he were still an on-the-street gatherer of information. Even the Konditorei Café had changed—more young business people and students—more group interaction—and very little intel. He recognized no one and found himself actually listening to the background music.

It had taken about three years for the Supreme Court's 1952 ruling to become effective while Wally was in the States. During this time, Party planning activities were overhauled to become more clandestine—operations more undercover.

Public recruiting rallies ended. Downtown Party offices that had been placed in easy-to-find little offices all over were now invisible, underground—and moved around from time to time to avoid detection. Communication engaged less writing, more word of mouth.

So by 1957-58, as he was reestablishing himself back into this familiar community, the buildings may have looked the same but sidewalk conversations had changed.

This time, Wally's job became more editorial, more professional...more intellectual. He associated with different kinds of people. His assignments weren't necessarily more predictable; they were just less surprising, less hazardous—less outside the building.

As Cold War issues became more complicated, army operations evolved as well. One of his duties required him to lead teams developing U.S. foreign procedures—measures suitable for addressing subtleties of jealous governments or fencing with counterparts' personalities. These were countries possessing atomic weapons in one pocket, and potential for reactionary mayhem in another. It wasn't like fencing with weapons; it was more like sparring with invisible swords casting damaging touchés with each risky prick or poke. Yesterday's contingency planning often didn't provide much this-morning solace.

What really did excite Wally were cutting-edge capabilities like in-the-sky surveillance, or intel retrieval from aerial photographs, or how new decoding technologies worked—in ways that were quite pioneering for the late 1950s. These were like once-in-awhile vitamins that kept him thinking ...and stimulated. What-if questions saturated his casual thinking.

But, mundane sides of a nine-to-five workaday meandered into and out of his in-baskets, and after-lunch schedules. Once paper was shuffled and mid-morning priorities carefully filed, there was always that one further complicating duty that had to be attended to. The one most often victim of his procrastinations dealt with creating classified manuals used in training or for general information processing—necessary, essential, but not much fun to prepare. His daily rhythmic mantra: write, edit, proofread, print, repeat.

Few subjects piqued Wally's interest outside those detailing his experiences and expertise. But these training guides were everyday textbooks, not stories. Although particular manuals became well-used and well-worn, sometimes he considered himself more a librarian than the professor he had become. These references, all bearing Wally's signature, were consumed by officers and enlisted alike; they became threadbare leather bibles utilized by anyone dealing with espionage for the U.S. Army. If you had a question, "...just ask Captain Rothwell."

Despite sterile-sounding names, by implication these projects dealt with rooting out spies or uncovering unacceptable activities. How to deal with such restricted information by qualified army management was why these manuals were necessary.

———

It wasn't until later in 1958 that he once again met Hilsa. It wasn't a planned event, but an unintended encounter just outside a newly opened café ...followed by mutual surprised smiles with eyes reading eyes, wondering about the five years that had just passed.

Wally gave a brief update on family and some newspaper stories he had written (supporting his previous journalist persona), but little else.

She mentioned having a new job, more money but little time to chat. Yet, "it was really nice to meet up once again" she said grasping his hand. "I have so much to tell you!" Not having time to chat was obviously disconcerting to both. Honestly happy to see each other, they made a quickly set date for the following week then she darted away in an unusual mission-oriented gait without looking back. His eyes lingered just for a moment. Her steps swished as her legs dodged others' before disappearing into the crowd.

When he asked about her "P" status back in his office on the Seventh Floor, he learned about how unofficially she had managed to start working inside the Party in some administrative role. *And*—he was informed by Colonel Jack quite explicitly—he was absolutely *not* to engage Hilsa in any conversations.

But Wally was interested. His argument that he had had a special relationship yielding good intel fell on deaf ears ...something else was happening—someone else was probably playing his own on-the-street role.

He skipped that quickly set up meeting with Hilsa. He wondered if she had showed.

——

One of his more essential but unexciting duties was Chief of the Polish Desk in Frankfurt for the 970th CIC. As analyst, he collected intel data then created detailed evaluations for use by other commanders. He directly supervised army intelligence operations inside Poland. But, this was mostly paperwork too.

There were temporary assignments too, like his mission as U.S. liaison coordinating efforts with German-French intelligence. Such unconventional things kept his brain active.

——

While Hilsa's name never came up at all, he presumed correctly that some Party intel must have been coming via her contributions. For the next couple of years, he would scrutinize various remarks from secret sources hoping to gain a clue to identity. Often written remarks would just fit her German speech—those word choices, references to certain players, and about locations they both knew in common. But it didn't matter; the remarks were of very low value.

Whereas she had been an on-the-street party sympathizer five years ago, she apparently was now a genuine employee—not in a particularly significant position perhaps, but one theoretically bumping elbows with others playing consequential, maybe far-reaching roles. Wally would ask questions about how the now-illegal Communist Party was operating; and, he'd always get privileged evidence, but her name never actually surfaced.

He worked on the Seventh Floor of that ugly gray, cement building. One of the more memorable things here was the open elevator. It even had a name, *pater nostra*. When translated, it revealed how one needed to pray for safety when using it. Everyone could see out from inside amidst the clinks and grunts and twangs of running chains and wire bands. Rube Goldberg would have been proud. Wally spent altogether too much time figuring out how the elevator worked.

In 1961 he was recognized for resolute spirit and effectiveness for getting all compelling army formats and vernacular onto paper. He was promoted to Major Walter H. Rothwell, Jr.

In 1962, Wally turned 39. He never saw Hilsa again; she faded away into the crowd of other "almost-insiders."

———

Since he could speak French fluently, his name was top of the preselection list to go to Vietnam in 1962. It was a logical next-step teaching interrogation techniques to army personnel who had started to muster in increasing numbers in South Vietnam. Having been appointed operations officer on the Special Military Advisory Team in Saigon, his underlying mission was to train Vietnamese troops in undercover intelligence techniques.

Only eight years prior, the French had grossly underestimated abilities of armed local dissidents, and were defeated at the embarrassing battle of Điên Biên Phũ.

Despite two or three generals inside the US Army's

European theater requesting Major Rothwell be assigned once again to Germany, they were overridden by other generals' interests for him to serve in Vietnam—a place that few in the intelligence community knew very much about.

Ever since Kennedy's bitter disagreement in 1961 with Nikita Khrushchev, Southeast Asia had moved from a page four to bottom of page stories on the front page two or three times a week. Placenames like Saigon, Da Nang and Hanoi were everyday words everyone could pronounce. For weeks, it seemed, *Time Magazine* had an editorial or story about the implications of JFK's "line in the sand." Newspaper stories grew longer, photographs donned magazine articles.

Within a year of Wally's arrival, army troop strength had augmented to 16,000 active military personnel stationed in South Vietnam up from Eisenhower's 900 advisors a couple years before.

Even though the Cold War had lingered on the edges of every political foray, Vietnam was now on-the-ground activity. Exactly what was happening was vital information to get and decipher. The U.S. couldn't rely on secondhand data. Too many unknowns were manifesting as combat phases began manifesting and multiplying.

Wally's assignments may have been predefined as "precautionary," but they could now be more accurately expressed as real preparatory measures for things foreseen by those wearing stars on their collars.

Unlike Germany, Thelma and the kids couldn't cross an ocean as family. Her assignment was to remain home for the year Wally would spend in Vietnam. Her mission became letter-writing and taking photographs for forwarding to Major Rothwell ten thousand miles away once a week.

———

Although Wally was stationed in Saigon, he journeyed to wherever inexperienced army officers needing specialized training happened to be. This is why he ended up trekking throughout the country to places like Natrang, Da Nang, Buôn Ma Thuột, and even onto the mountain slopes where the Montagnards (an important information source) inhabited.

Montagnards were native Asian tribal groups inhabiting mountainsides along Cambodian and Laotian borders with Vietnam. Sometimes called Highlanders or Mountain People, their potential value had to be exploited by the South Vietnamese army. Once war activities had commenced, Montagnard participation became significant because their presence turned out to be an effective roadblock on the Viet Cong's southbound resupply route, the Ho Chi Minh Trail as well as information source.

Wally's specific job was to direct three or four teams who would in turn inspect and advise U.S. troops about military intelligence proficiencies.

Though strictly advisory roles, Wally and his teams also trained South Vietnamese military how to penetrate Viet Cong intruders and handle captured VCs. Since many educated Vietnamese military knew French, Wally's role was surprisingly more effective than what it would have been only in English, and distinctive among counterpart officers inside the army's entourage.

But the U.S. Army really had two distinctly different missions in Vietnam.

The first was the very public one designed to advise Vietnamese officers using specific models and experience. These were classroom-type instructions as well as on-the-job examples when a Viet Cong (VC) combatant was encountered. He associated with the French intelligentsia who still lived in southern Vietnam, and would often participate in social events. Being able to speak French so well, he was able to grasp political subtleties others could not.

But consequential and a more *sub rosa* role was to collect intelligence for the U.S. army. They found amendable locals from whom information was extracted in friendly ways. They expanded efforts by crafting relationships that turned into networks of viable moles. Ultimately, Wally's interactions were more like U.S. agents than teachers, more like American spies than patrons supporting the Vietnamese.

This may be why he fit into his role so well even though he didn't really add Vietnamese onto his menu of languages spoken.

Professional fluencies centered on exchanging information ...to and from people on the street—people choosing what role to play inside their own anxieties in the middle of a deteriorating, hostile environment—among people learning how to survive yet once again. In twelve calendar months, Wally helped set the stage for the performances yet to come inside that Vietnam Theater.

19

Seated aboard the plane heading east, Wally again reflected upon all that was going on in his home country. It was 1963, conflicts in Vietnam were escalating frantically, strategies were plentiful but explanations emerged vague. There were so many people critical of the war. This wasn't Europe or Korea— why were we spending lives and wealth in this ambiguous Asian country?

Was he merely one of many tactics employed? Or was he part of the solution …or maybe at least the resolution? Reflection often produced doubt. But he embraced personal resolve despite social public unrest.

President Kennedy would be assassinated later on that fall. After another few months of remembrances and unfulfilled programs, it didn't take very long for President Lyndon B. Johnson to begin his own personal debut about a formidable, even more progressive agenda tailored for a U.S. domestic audience.

But, even though thinking he'd rather be busy with a new era of progressive domestic affairs, LBJ couldn't get Southeast Asia out of his in-basket. He may have been president, but he wasn't really sure who was listening to him.

After Major Rothwell re-crossed the Pacific, he rejoined his family in Baltimore. "Home" it might be, but it still seemed foreign to what he had become culturally accustomed to over the last more than forty years, almost all in Europe. He and his family were indeed an international foursome by birth, language, culture, and outlook—even though American in heart.

But America was in disarray, deteriorating, reformatting into something different ... but what?

On one hand, American colleges and cities were restless with anti-war sentiments as the sheer numbers of "next" soldiers, marines, and sailors needed for war lined up. Troop counts escalated repeatedly. Weapons shipments, tanks and ammunition—and troops—were newsworthy and intimidating to many. Pros and cons topped page one of the news daily. On the other hand, number counts of green plastic bags bearing remains of those caught in the crossfire kept increasing every month too. The country was divided.

Upon checking in at Fort Holabird, his next assignment was ready. The very next day, he began attending the Field Operations Intelligence (FOI) course. Immediately upon graduation a few weeks later, he was appointed operations officer for the entire FOI department at the Intelligence School—a position he'd hold for three years.

With know-hows under his belt, Wally had become professor emeritus in the field of espionage. His opinion mattered. Experience was valued in the classroom, and his credentials were sought and exploited wherever they could be. In such high-demand and amid sizeable public skepticism, Wally felt he had indeed become part of the resolution.

Promotion Ceremony - May 1965: Colonel Derzis and Wally's wife, Thelma Rothwell awarding LtCol Walter Rothwell his new rank

Wally and Thelma now took time to explore other parts of Europe. They especially enjoyed touring Spain and Morocco—even bought a nice hand-woven rug in Casablanca.

In May 1965, he became Lieutenant Colonel Walter Rothwell Jr. It was during this time Wally had been sought by the European Command to assist negotiations with the German government establishing U.S. Army maneuvering rights in central Europe. Tangible results of these complex negotiations continue to survive in place even to this day.

In May 1967, as lieutenant colonel, Wally decided to retire and requested a nonmilitary position in the same field. He had been successfully "converted" into a good administrator—a leader-type bureaucrat in the schools of future spies.

His application reached the desk of the top Pentagon intelligence general who decided his talent best used by transferring, once again, to West Germany. Promoted to GS-13, he was assigned to the 18th MI (Military Intelligence) Battalion as Special Advisor to the Battalion Commander, and held the position for five years. He and his family lived in Frankfurt.

The Special Advisor designation had been created for and tailored to Wally's skills. Many duties used his cross-cultural aptitude for working with European officials like the Belgian Army Chief of Staff, or overseeing American civilians working in Berlin, Frankfurt, Giessen, and other cities around West Germany. Though civilian, he conducted tasks with astute military orientation working with both West German and U.S. Army's Intelligence staff.

Performance seemed to be measured by how fast paper passed through in-baskets ...though no one ever said this. Pats on the back from star-lapelled decision-makers were more like corporate CEOs' praise for profitability rather than strategic military value. It was no longer about a nameplate on his desk or those business cards that used to be stashed away for some far more interesting reason.

Privately, he struggled being the has-been bureaucrat he had already become. But now, the new tightlipped mission was learning how to acquiesce with his Wally-esque smile.

———

During the mid-1960s, college campuses carried raw ingredients to the media kitchen every day. Magazine editors and newspaper headlines seasoned this stewpot of controversy with each new edition. Lyndon Johnson decided not to run for reelection in 1968.

Over the next few years as LBJ's war was replaced by Nixon's war, civic restiveness evolved into public agitation then into outright on-the-street protests. Every college student had an opinion. Some young men "escaped" to Canada to avoid confronting such a war without their permission. Some reveled by receiving high draft priority numbers[5] while others rebelled against parents by enlisting just to get out of town. There was flag-waving on one side of the street, and flag-burning on the other.

To what extent the to-go or not-to-go decisions were actually patriotic could be debated. At least by the early 1970s, the draft had been eliminated. Troops were coming home.

The U.S. was still evaluating what was gained and lost by this East Asian investment. No matter what the reason, this skinny serpentine-shaped, previously unidentifiable country was the trigger for passionate opinion—passions fading only as the 1970s inched by.

Front page stories were eventually replaced by other headlines.

———

In 1972 upon his return to the U.S. yet again, Wally was assigned to Fort Huachuca, Arizona, serving as Chief of the Systems Integration Branch. The unit's mission was integrating aerial surveillance and communications systems applied to tactical units.

Though now living full time in Arizona, he traveled to Belgium on several occasions. Mr. Walter Rothwell represented the U.S. intelligence community at NATO Headquarters—specifically chosen to develop a tactical intelligence doctrine—a standardized high-level protocol for use among conferring nations. The mission was to provide interoperability among the participating leadership and achieve ongoing mutual agreements.

Belgian General Henry Vanreckom, *L'Armee Secrete,* became Wally's personal friend. General Vanreckom had been in charge of the Resistance Movement in Belgium. Wally and his family were often the General's personal guests in Brussels. When he visited the U.S., Wally was always assigned as his personal escort even

---

[5] Males eligible for military service received a random number based upon their date of birth. Those with the lowest numbers were inducted first; those with high numbers just waited it out and were not drafted.

though a civilian.

———

Late afternoon in August 1984, another decision was being pondered …then ultimately devised. Clouds blackened the southern sky with an imminent Arizona monsoon-type storm coming in.

It was time.

Bureaucrats play important roles for sure, but Wally thoughtfully reminisced about sipping another *mohrenkopf* or two—gaining information, putting strategic riddles together to make sense, acquiring insights others could not—all while staring out the window now dotting with thudding drops. It was pelting Arizona rain …his vision blurred as water streaked down the panes …his eyes meshed with the image. Moisture lingered below his eyelids.

It was time.

Indeed, it was more about the hunt.

…the chase.

… the puzzle solved.

———

After serving eighteen years as a civilian and twenty-two in the U.S. Army, Wally retired from his post in 1985 at Fort Huachuca. Virtually his entire forty year career was in one form of military intelligence or another.

By this time, with daughters grown, Wally and Thelma had begun to travel for the sake of visiting places for their own attraction. Though Wally had no remaining close family connections of his own beyond his wife and daughters, he and Thelma made several trips to Saskatchewan to visit with her family. They crossed the Atlantic three different times taking in Spain, France and Germany as tourists and spending leisure time at Normandy, the Matterhorn …including a long and poignant stopover to Lugano in Switzerland.

But outside his family and among only a few who had a need-to-know reason, nobody really knew what he did for a career or the starring roles he played—few even knew him as a person, much less about the roads he traversed. Wally never talked about all those muddy tin-can alleys or murky pitch-black closets, or much about the merits or consequences of doors he unlocked or doors he helped close. Ah, those were the days!

It's not that he was hidden ...he had been conspicuously inconspicuous.

It's not that he was limelighted by much onstage drama— it wasn't about the applause ...it was and continued to be, well, the "*sub rosa*"—about what happened under the rose—about those unobvious things that actually happened—events that changed political or military decisions, people that counted, consequences that mattered. But now...

...the ultimate battles are not against others but with self ...seldom about what we lose but about what we can't take with us ...less about time well-spent than about clocks.

Epilogue

I got to know Wally Rothwell on his 90th birthday. A neighbor, he was celebrating his decades with family and friends at a special party in late spring, 2013.

Responsible for our Arizona-oriented neighborhood newsletter called *Javalina.Line,* I took some photos with my cellphone and wrote a story about this special local event. He lived directly across the street from my wife and me. An engaging sort, he mentioned how long he had lived on the street, about his late wife—his beautiful Thelma in every other sentence. He and I looked across his walls of photographs and remembrances. He wanted us to know how comfortable retirement had been since arriving in Tucson.

When I interviewed him for our newsletter story, I imagined it would be twenty to thirty minutes. I asked about his employment. He mentioned how he had grown up in Europe, college during World War II, his early army years, Cold War events and diplomacy, and his roles as a military instructor. There was always another "and" and another comment followed. I would say "tell me more" and he did. It made for a good story that virtually no one on the street had considered.

I'd bump into him regularly at the row of mailboxes less than 200 feet from our homes—he was not able to walk far easily, so he drove his car to get mail—still a rather cumbersome ordeal. He always smiled and had something friendly to say to anyone passing by. Hand-waving became a repetitious daily habit, comment-exchanging a frequent event.

His last employment had been in Sierra Vista (about an hour southeast), so Tucson was a logical retirement choice as it turned out to be for a great many of us in the Village—close to shopping, scores of medical offices and a hospital nearby, a library within walking distance, plus a lot of seniors who for years liked to walk around on the streets.

———

Later in 2014, after he finished reading my book, *Just Dust*, a memoir about my own sojourn to Southeast Asia in the 1960s, we were chatting about the *Javalina.Line* story celebrating his 90th birthday a year prior. He too had been to Vietnam, he went on to describe assignments during the early 1960s.

He produced two typewritten pages outlining key events without much elaboration. The paper was marked up and wrinkled from repeated foldings. I read through bullet-pointed paragraphs rather quickly.

He then asked me if I would be willing to write down a few more pages about these events. I asked deeper questions which resulted in more stories, which prompted more questions, until I succumbed. I became captivated by images and depictions of his rambling down narrow but fascinating paths, by encountering people and events I had seen in history books, and eventually mesmerized by unassuming verbal pictures of clandestine and consequential activities. Seeking no glamor or publicity, he let his own character remain in the shade unseen while significant events labored on all around him. Wally indeed lived inconspicuously *under the rose.*

A modest man, now 92, he underscored his own contractual promises to uphold the pertinent secrecies inside his missions during those historically awkward times in the 1950s.

On one hand, he downplayed the limelight about the significance of his own roles, quick to point out the value of others' achievements.

On the other hand, he seemed to rest his eyes on the merits of these roads less traveled—roads with unique outcomes, something personally satisfying and perhaps worthy enough to document.

Once when I was talking about heritage, the spontaneous answer was "American" of course; but, then he paused, raising his hand to signal he was thinking.

"Y'know?" pausing again, "I think I hafta say the Swiss culture impacted me more than any other considering my age at the time, attending high school there, learning French, and how language played the role it did. Educated Germans tried to speak their language like the Swiss did. High German is more Swiss like, more guttural, more precise." He looked up.

Putting his thumb and forefinger to his cheeks, rubbing his unshaved chin, he began pondering back seventy-five years. "It was like they were coughing up phlegm!"

Then he mused. "It reminds me of a story by Swiss author, Diccon Bewes. Let me try to find it." A couple minutes later, he opened the book and read me this passage quoting from Bewes' book, *Swiss Watching*, about how Swiss German meshed with English.

Perhaps the trickiest part of Advanced Swinglish to master is the pronunciation. It seems just like English, but small variations make all the difference. I found that out the hard way when I started work in the Stauffacher English Bookshop:

Swiss customer: I need a book on cheeses.

Me: Okay, I'll show you what we have.

In the Cookery section, I get out three books on cheese.

Customer, shaking her head: Not cheese. CHEE-SES.

At this point, I am wondering if cheese has a plural. Was it like sheep, with none? Or more like fish, plural when more than one type is involved? Or was this a Swinglish plural, like informations? Not wanting to get in a discussion on that, I try again, going with the plural in the hope that it helps.

Me: So you are looking for something about cheeses?

Customer: Yes. Books on holey cheeses.

Me, smiling: Ah, a book on Swiss cheeses!

Customer, looking at me as if I am simple: There is no Swiss cheeses.

Me, now wondering about a singular verb with a plural noun: We do have some books on Swiss cheeses.

Customer, very irritated: Cheeses was not Swiss. He was the Son of God.

Me, finally catching up: Oh you mean, Jesus.

Customer: Yes, this is what I have been saying. A book on cheeses.

Wally mused on, "y' know, I like cheese fondue, and gruyere is always the best to use here in the States. But if you're in Switzerland, use *opizeller* or *emmentalar* cheese."

This is how it went with Wally. Despite challenges with hearing, despite labored methodical speech, he'd breathe and pause then glance up smiling and ever so slightly wink his eye with his uniquely his I-know-what-you're-thinking smile. He knew I was listening. He said, "...my language as well as my life's been like that 'Swinglish', y'know?"

All said and done, I could tell he enjoyed his journeys harvesting story upon story, recollection upon recollection obviously unlike very many others' remembrances. This spirit of vitality and humor was revealed to me.

Turning his thoughts into words, then placing the memories onto paper became a reward to share with those who participated in or remembered where his life had led him—and a good story of *what-might-be*'s for those who didn't.

What a gift to me it was to be awarded the pen to write it down!

Bibliography

Bewes, Diccon. *Swiss Watching: Inside the Land of Milk & Money;* Nicholas Brealey Publishing, Second Edition, 2012.

Schallert, Edwin. *Philharmonic Makes Debut; New Orchestra Raises Tone of Local Music;* Los Angeles Times, October 25, 1919.

Simon, Henry W. *100 Great Operas and their stories.* Act-by act synopses originally published as "Festival of Opera" by Doubleday & Company in 1957. Dolphin Books edition, 1960.

Smith, Caroline Estes. *The Philharmonic Orchestra of Los Angeles,* "The First Decade" 1919-1929; United Printing Company, 1930.

Wikipedia. Various verifications of incidental dates, locations, and placenames.

Winterbotham, F.W. *The Ultra Secret;* Dell Publishing Co, Inc., 1975.

About the Author

Wes Choc grew up in Albuquerque, New Mexico, living there until 1965 when he joined the Marine Corps during the Vietnam era. Since the end of his military service in 1969, he worked for the American Automobile Association for over forty years. In 1992 he was appointed president and CEO of AAA MountainWest, overseeing business and club operations in Montana, Wyoming, and Alaska. After retiring from AAA in 2008, he and his wife, Carol, moved to Arizona.

Wes has become an active community volunteer. With his TEFL certificate in hand, he spent three months teaching English as a second language in Ecuador. Back at home, Wes tutors English regularly for new US residents. He also mentors homeless and troubled youth.

Wes has worked with veterans in Montana and Arizona, especially with vets returning from overseas with PTSD or other disabilities. He is currently an active volunteer at the Tucson Veterans' Hospital helping recovering vets.

Wes enjoys writing and has recently established his own publishing platform aptly named Chosen Journey Media. With his initial success of "Just Dust – An Improbable Marine's Story", Wes went back to work and is delighted to have completed "Inconspicuous" as a life story told to him by a friend who also served the United States proudly in uniform.

Carol and Wes Choc make their home in Tucson, Arizona.

CPSIA information can be obtained
at www.ICGtesting.com
Printed in the USA
FSOW02n0555200217
30922FS

INCONSPICUOUS

My first work, *Just Dust: An Improbable Marine's Vietnam Story* is my personal heartfelt journey during an audacious period of US history . . . about seeing war and trekking many "roads less traveled" than most other young military men ever do.

More recently, I innocently befriended a neighbor, Walter Rothwell. Unknowingly, our encounters turned into hours of chatting with Wally about his own journey. I had no idea I lived near a spy . . . not just a spy of consequence but one with a story worth telling!

So, I present to you Wally's journey . . . *Inconspicuous*.

WALTER H. ROTHWELL, JR. Drafted into the military the same month World War II ended might seem fortuitous, but because of Private Wally Rothwell's shrewd ability to speak four languages like a native, it enticed him into a world of strategic intelligence ...and ultimately Cold War espionage. He was a spy. He earned rank as well as prestige as a go-to person for unearthing worthy information. From gumshoe to classroom instructor ...from authority of on-the-street mole tactics to eventually delivering necessary backup for momentous Cold War decisions in 1952, Rothwell delivered consequence ...inconspicuously. Being an escort of European generals ...or early-on spy trainer in Vietnam ...or US emissary for NATO in Belgium, Wally retired a Lieutenant Colonel and expert in his field after 22 years in the US Army.

Chosen Journey MEDIA

Tuscon, Arizona

$14.99

ISBN 978-0-9964179-2-1

51499>

9 780996 417921

FROM **AIMLESS**
TO **AMAZING**

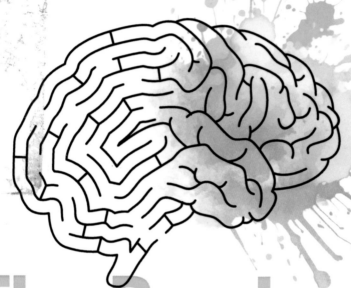

The Rewire
Retirement
Method

CYN MEYER